W9-CVA-339

OREGON FOCUS ON

Linear Equations

SM curriculum

Stage 3

AUTHORS

SHANNON McCAW

BETH ARMSTRONG • MATT McCAW • SARAH SCHUHL • MICHELLE TERRY • SCOTT VALWAY

COVER PHOTOGRAPH

Crater Lake

The deepest lake in the United States, Crater Lake
was formed from the eruption of Mt. Mazama
over 7,000 years ago. Set in the Cascade Mountain
Range in the Southern portion of the state,
Crater Lake was the seventh area in the
United States designated as a national park.
©iStockphoto.com/Elena Korenbaum

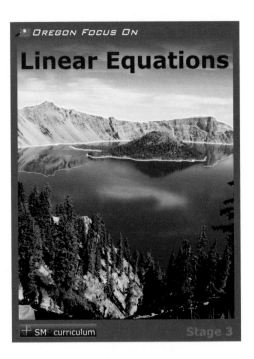

Copyright ©2008 by SM^c Curriculum LLC. All rights reserved. Printed in U.S.A. This publication is protected by copyright. No part of this publication should be reproduced or transmitted in any form or by any means without prior written consent of the publisher. This includes, but is not limited to, electronic reproduction, storage in a retrieval system, photocopying, recording or broadcasting for distance learning. For information regarding permission(s), write to: Permissions Department.

ISBN: 978-1-935033-08-0

4 5 6 7 8 9 10

ABOUT THE AUTHORS

SERIES AUTHOR

Shannon McCaw is a classroom teacher and consultant. She has taught mathematics in the Newberg and Parkrose School Districts. She has been trained in Professional Learning Communities, Differentiated Instruction and Critical Friends. Shannon currently works with math teachers from over 40 districts around the State of Oregon. Her expertise lies in Oregon standards, curriculum alignment and assessment practices. Shannon has a Masters of Arts in Secondary Math Education from Colorado College.

CONTRIBUTING AUTHORS

Beth Armstrong has been an elementary school teacher in the Beaverton School District. She has received training in Talented and Gifted Instruction. She recently completed her Masters in Curriculum and Instruction from Washington State University.

Matt McCaw has been a classroom teacher and special education case-manager in the Newberg, Centennial and Parkrose School Districts in Oregon. Matt has been trained in Differentiated Instruction, Professional Learning Communities, Critical Friends Groups and Understanding Poverty. He currently teaches math at Parkrose High School. Matt has a Masters of Special Education from Western Oregon University.

Sarah Schuhl has been a classroom teacher in Union, Lake Oswego and Centennial School Districts in Oregon. She has been trained in Assessment for Learning, Professional Learning Communities, Advanced Placement and Instructional Coaching. She currently serves as the Math Instructional Coach at Centennial High School. Sarah has a Masters of Science in Teaching Mathematics from Portland State University.

Michelle Terry has been a classroom teacher in the Estacada and Newberg School Districts in Oregon. Michelle has received training in Professional Learning Communities, Critical Friends, and ELL Instructional Strategies. Michelle has an Interdisciplinary Masters from Western Oregon University. She currently fills the role of a Teacher on Special Assignment with a focus on math curriculum and instruction at Newberg High School.

Scott Valway has been a classroom teacher in the Tigard-Tualatin, Newberg and Parkrose School Districts in Oregon. Scott has been trained in Differentiated Instruction, Professional Learning Communities, Critical Friends, Discovering Algebra, and Pre-Advanced Placement. Scott has a Masters of Science in Teaching from Oregon State University. He currently teaches math at Parkrose High School.

OREGON CORE STANDARDS

The complete set of Oregon Core Standards can be found at www.ode.state.or.us/go/math. This book focuses on the highlighted core standards shown below.

GRADE 8

It is essential that these standards be addressed in contexts that promote problem solving, reasoning, communication, making connections, and designing and analyzing representations.

8.1	**Algebra: Analyze and represent linear functions, and solve linear equations and systems of linear equations.**
8.1.1	Translate among contextual, verbal, tabular, graphical, and algebraic representations of linear functions.
8.1.2	Determine the slope of a line and understand that it is a constant rate of change.
8.1.3	Identify and interpret the properties (i.e. slope, intercepts, continuity, and discreteness) of linear relationships as they are shown in the different representations and recognize proportional relationships ($y/x = k$ or $y = kx$) as a special case.
8.1.4	Use linear functions and equations to represent, analyze and solve problems, and to make predictions and inferences.
8.1.5	Relate systems of two linear equations in two variables and their solutions to pairs of lines that are intersecting, parallel, or the same line.
8.1.6	Use informal strategies (e.g., graphs or tables) to solve problems involving systems of linear equations in two variables.

8.2	**Data Analysis and Algebra: Analyze and summarize data sets.**
8.2.1	Organize and display data (e.g., histograms, box-and-whisker plots, scatter plots) to pose and answer questions; and justify the reasonableness of the choice of display.
8.2.2	Use measures of center and spread to summarize and compare data sets.
8.2.3	Interpret and analyze displays of data and descriptive statistics.
8.2.4	Compare descriptive statistics and evaluate how changes in data affect those statistics.
8.2.5	Describe the strengths and limitations of a particular statistical measure, and justify or critique its use in a given situation.
8.2.6	Use sample data to make predictions regarding a population.
8.2.7	Identify claims based on statistical data and evaluate the reasonableness of those claims.
8.2.8	Use data to estimate the likelihood of future events and evaluate the reasonableness of predictions.

8.3	**Geometry and Measurement: Analyze two- and three-dimensional spaces and figures by using distance and angle.**
8.3.1	Use properties of parallel lines, transversals, and angles to find missing sides and angles, and to solve problems including determining similarity or congruence of triangles.
8.3.2	Use models to show that the sum of the angles of any triangle is 180 degrees and apply this fact to find unknown angles.
8.3.3	Use models and logical arguments to show that the sum of the angles of any quadrilateral is 360 degrees, and apply this fact to find unknown angles
8.3.4	Use models to explore the validity of the Pythagorean Theorem, and use it to find missing lengths.
8.3.5	Apply the Pythagorean Theorem to find distances in a variety of 2- and 3-dimensional contexts, including distances on coordinate graphs.
8.3.6	Use models and referents to explore and estimate square roots.

Reprinted with permission from the Oregon Department of Education. All rights reserved.

OREGON FOCUS ON LINEAR EQUATIONS

CONTENTS IN BRIEF

Block 1 ~ Expressions and Equations

Block 2 ~ Sequences and Slope

BLOCK 3 ~ USING LINEAR EQUATIONS

BLOCK 4 ~ SYSTEMS OF EQUATIONS

HOW TO USE YOUR MATH BOOK

Your math book has features that will help you be successful in this course. Use this guide to help you understand how to use this book.

LESSON TARGET

 Look in this box at the beginning of every lesson to know what you will be learning about in each lesson.

VOCABULARY

Each new vocabulary word is printed in red. The definition can be found with the word. You can also find the definition of the word in the glossary which is in the back of this book.

EXPLORE!

Some lessons have **EXPLORE!** activities which allow you to discover mathematical concepts. Look for these activities in the Table of Contents and in lessons next to the purple line.

EXAMPLES

Examples are useful because they remind you how to work through different types of problems. Look for the word **EXAMPLE** and the green line.

HELPFUL HINTS

Helpful hints and important things to remember can be found in green callout boxes.

BLUE BOXES

A blue box holds important information or a process that will be used in that lesson. Not every lesson has a blue box.

 This calculator icon will appear in Lessons and Exercises where a calculator is needed. Your teacher may want you to use your calculator at other times, too. If you are unsure, make sure to ask if it is the right time to use it.

EXERCISES

The **EXERCISES** are a place for you to find practice problems to determine if you understand the lesson's target. You can find selected answers in the back of this book so you can check your progress.

REVIEW

The **REVIEW** provides a set of problems for you to practice concepts you have already learned in this book. The **REVIEW** follows the **EXERCISES** in each lesson. There is also a **REVIEW** section at the end of each Block.

TIC-TAC-TOE ACTIVITIES

Each Block has a Tic-Tac-Toe board at the beginning with activities that extend beyond the Oregon Core Standards. The Tic-Tac-Toe activities described on the board can be found throughout each Block in yellow boxes.

CAREER FOCUS

At the end of each Block, you will find an autobiography of an Oregon resident. Each person explains what they like about their job and how math is used in their career.

OREGON FOCUS ON MATH
STAGE 3

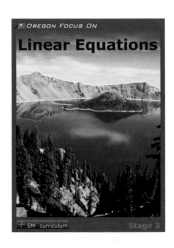

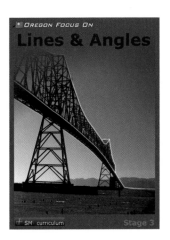

LETTER FROM THE AUTHORS

Dear Student,

This textbook was specifically designed for you. As a student learning math in Oregon, you are responsible for learning three areas of mathematics each year. Each year you will take a state assessment that tests your skills in these areas.

Stage 1	*Focus on Fractions and Decimals*
	Focus on Ratios, Rates and Percents
	Focus on Introductory Algebra
Stage 2	*Focus on Rational Numbers and Equations*
	Focus on Proportionality
	Focus on Surface Area and Volume
Stage 3	*Focus on Linear Equations*
	Focus on Data Analysis
	Focus on Lines and Angles

When you successfully finish these areas, you will be ready to enter Algebra I. For the graduating class of 2014 and beyond, you will need 3 credits of mathematics in high school that are at the Algebra I level and above.

It is important that you give your best effort in math class as everyone can be good at math if they try. If you have questions, ask your teacher, a friend or a parent. Do not be shy; nearly everyone struggles with math sometimes.

In these books you will find information about places and events from all across the state of Oregon. We hope you enjoy learning about your state. You may even find something about the city or town you live in!

Sincerely,

Shannon McCaw

Matt McCaw

Beth Armstrong

Sarah Schuhl

Scott Valway

Michelle Terry

BLOCK 1 ~ LINEAR EQUATIONS
EXPRESSIONS AND EQUATIONS

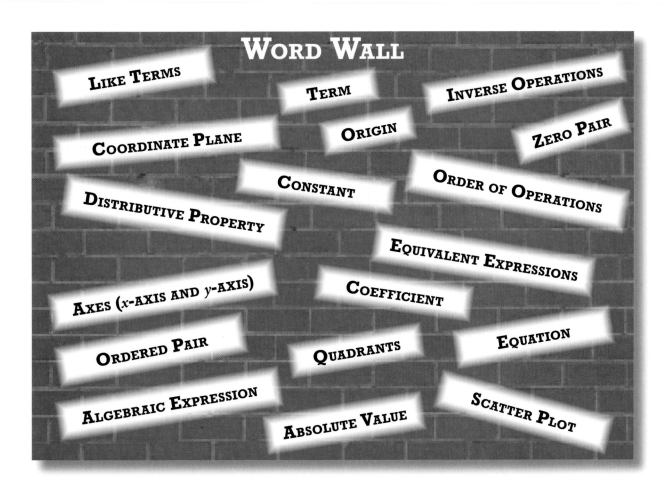

WORD WALL

LIKE TERMS

TERM

INVERSE OPERATIONS

COORDINATE PLANE

ORIGIN

ZERO PAIR

CONSTANT

ORDER OF OPERATIONS

DISTRIBUTIVE PROPERTY

EQUIVALENT EXPRESSIONS

AXES (*x*-AXIS AND *y*-AXIS)

COEFFICIENT

ORDERED PAIR

QUADRANTS

EQUATION

ALGEBRAIC EXPRESSION

ABSOLUTE VALUE

SCATTER PLOT

BLOCK 1 ~ EXPRESSIONS AND EQUATIONS
TIC - TAC - TOE

WHAT'S THE PROCESS? Create a poster that explains the process of solving a multi-step equation. *See page 25 for details.*	**SMALL BUSINESS PROFITS** Study three different business start-up plans. Determine how many items the business will need to sell to break even and make a profit. *See page 31 for details.*	**ORDER OF OPS POETRY** Write three different poems about the order of operations. *See page 15 for details.*
LIKE TERMS GAME Create a matching game requiring players to combine like terms to make pairs. *See page 15 for details.*	**SCATTER PLOT SURVEY** Conduct a survey and record your results on a scatter plot. Determine if there is a correlation between the items. *See page 36 for details.*	**TEMPERATURE SYSTEMS** Convert temperatures from one system to another. *See page 25 for details.*
EQUATION MATS Produce a "How To..." guide to show others how to use equation mats to solve a variety of equations. *See page 31 for details.*	**INEQUALITIES** Solve inequalities and graph solutions on a number line.  *See page 37 for details.*	**SCIENTIFIC NOTATION** Learn to write very large and very small numbers in scientific notation.  *See page 6 for details.*

ORDER OF OPERATIONS

Find the value of expressions using the order of operations.

Mr. Marshall asked his students to find the value of the expression

$$7 + 2 \cdot 3 - 1$$

Sasha is positive that the answer is 26. Michelle believes the answer is 12. Mr. Marshall has both students show their work on the board. Look at their work below. Who do you agree with? Why?

Sasha	Michelle
$7 + 2 \cdot 3 - 1$	$7 + 2 \cdot 3 - 1$
$= 9 \cdot 3 - 1$	$= 7 + 6 - 1$
$= 27 - 1$	$= 13 - 1$
$= 26$	$= 12$

Mathematicians have established an order of operations. The order of operations is a set of rules which are followed when evaluating an expression with more than one operation. Using the correct order of operations helped Michelle find the correct answer to Mr. Marshall's question because she multiplied before adding or subtracting.

ORDER OF OPERATIONS

1. Find the value of expressions inside grouping symbols such as parentheses, absolute value bars and fraction bars.
2. Find the value of all powers.
3. Multiply and divide from left to right.
4. Add and subtract from left to right.

All operations within grouping symbols must be completed before any of the other steps are completed. The three types of grouping symbols you will work with in this book are parentheses, absolute value bars and fraction bars.

Absolute value is the distance a number is from zero. The absolute value of a number is always positive. For example:

$$|-9 + 4| = |-5| = 5$$

The fraction bar is another symbol used to represent division. Perform all operations in the numerator and denominator before dividing. For example:

$$\frac{2 + 10}{5 - 1} = \frac{12}{4} = 3$$

EXAMPLE 1

Find the value of each expression.
a. $8(-3 + 7) - 2 \cdot 5$
b. $5^2 + |3 - 8| \div 5$

SOLUTIONS

a. Add the integers inside the parentheses. $8(-3 + 7) - 2 \cdot 5$ $= 8(4) - 2 \cdot 5$
Multiply from left to right. $= 32 - 10$
Subtract. $= 22$

b. Subtract inside the absolute value bars. $5^2 + |3 - 8| \div 5$ $= 5^2 + |-5| \div 5$
Make the value inside the bars positive. $= 5^2 + 5 \div 5$
Find the value of the power. $= 25 + 5 \div 5$
Divide. $= 25 + 1$
Add. $= 26$

EXAMPLE 2

Find the value of the expression.

$$\frac{(-5 - 3)^2}{6 - 4} - 50$$

SOLUTION

Perform operation inside the parentheses. $\dfrac{(-5 - 3)^2}{6 - 4} - 50$ $= \dfrac{(-8)^2}{6 - 4} - 50$

Find the value of $(-8)^2$. $= \dfrac{64}{6 - 4} - 50$

Subtract in the denominator. $= \dfrac{64}{2} - 50$

Divide numerator by denominator. $= 32 - 50$

Subtract. $= -18$

EXAMPLE 3

Jakim's family took a vacation to California. The plane tickets cost a total of $840, the hotel cost $250 and gas cost $130. There are 5 people in Jakim's family.
a. Write an expression that could be used to find the cost per person.
b. Find the cost per person.

SOLUTIONS

a. The numbers must be added before dividing by the number of people.
Use parentheses or the fraction bar to group the numbers that must be added.

$(840 + 250 + 130) \div 5$ OR $\dfrac{840 + 250 + 130}{5}$

b. $\dfrac{840 + 250 + 130}{5} = \dfrac{1220}{5} = \$244$

The vacation cost $244 per person.

EXERCISES

1. Nathan and Takashi each evaluated the expression $16 - 5 \cdot 2 + 4$. Nathan believes the solution is 10. Takashi disagrees and says the answer is 26.

    a. Who is correct? What operation did he perform first?

    b. What operation was done first by the student who was incorrect?

Evaluate each expression.

2. $18 \div 2 + 7 \cdot 3$

3. $6 \cdot 5 - 4 \div 2$

4. $(3 + 5)^2 - 8 \cdot 3$

5. $45 \div (-3)^2 + 4(2 + 1)$

6. $5 + 4|-2 + 8|$

7. $5(11 + 1) - 3(2 + 11)$

8. $12 - 2 \cdot 10 \div 5 - 1$

9. $|3 - 27| \div |4 + 2|$

10. $21 \div 3 \cdot 7 - 4^2$

Evaluate each expression.

11. $\dfrac{4 + 28}{6 - 2}$

12. $\dfrac{20(7 - 3)}{2 \cdot 5} - 7$

13. $\dfrac{|-18 + 3|}{9 - 6}$

14. $31 - \dfrac{5 + 4 \cdot 5 - 1}{2}$

15. $\dfrac{6(9 - 7)^2}{-2}$

16. $\dfrac{25}{5} - \dfrac{10|5 - 1|}{2}$

17. The Chess Club is selling tickets to Saturday's Winter Ball. Admission with Student ID is $5 per person. Admission without a Student ID is $8. The Chess Club sold 130 tickets to students with an ID Card and 40 tickets to students without ID Cards.

    a. Write an expression to represent the total amount of money the Chess Club collected in ticket sales.

    b. How much money did the Chess Club collect?

18. Four friends ordered Chinese food for dinner. The Kung Pao Chicken cost $11. The Sweet and Sour Pork cost $8 and the Mongolian Beef cost $13. The friends want to split the cost equally.

    a. Write an expression that could be used to find the cost per person.

    b. Find the cost per person.

19. Explain why it is necessary to have an order of operations in mathematics.

20. Create an expression with at least five numbers and two different operations that has a value of 15.

Insert one set of parentheses in each numerical expression so that it equals the stated amount.

21. $6 + 3 + 11 \div 4 = 5$

22. $7 + 1 \cdot 4 - 2 \cdot 5 = 17$

23. $-1 \cdot 6 + 8 - 4 \div 2 + 2 = 1$

Tic-Tac-Toe ~ Scientific Notation

Scientific notation is a method used by scientists and mathematicians to express very large and very small numbers. Scientific notation is an exponential expression using a power of 10.

$$N \times 10^P$$

Use the following process to convert a large or small number into scientific notation:

Step 1: Locate the decimal point and move it left or right so there is only one non-zero digit to its left. This number represents the value of N.

Step 2: Count the number of places that you moved the decimal point in **Step 1**. This number represents the value of P. If you move the decimal point to the left, the sign of P is positive. If you move the decimal point to the right, the sign of P is negative.

For example:

A. Convert 52,000 to scientific notation.

    Step 1: Move the decimal point to the **left** so there is only one non-zero digit to its left.
        52,000 → 5.2

    Step 2: Count how many places the decimal point was moved in the number above.
        5 2 0 0 0.

        The decimal point was moved 4 places to the **left**. Since the decimal point was moved left, the P value is positive. Scientific notation for 52,000 is 5.2×10^4.

B. Convert 0.00492 to scientific notation.

    Step 1: Move the decimal point to the **right** so there is only one non-zero digit to its left.
        0.00492

    Step 2: Count how many places the decimal point was moved in the number above.
        0. 0 0 4 9 2 → 4.92

        The decimal point was moved 3 places to the **right**. Since the decimal point was moved right, the P value is negative. Scientific notation for 0.00492 is 4.92×10^{-3}.

Write each large or small number in scientific notation.

1. 0.0049
2. 70,000
3. 5,930,000,000
4. 0.00821
5. 0.0000001
6. 320,000
7. 680
8. 0.00105
9. 75,000
10. When will numbers in scientific notation have a positive power of 10? When will the power of 10 be negative?
11. Keely wrote the number 9,200,000 in scientific notation. She incorrectly wrote the number as 92×10^5. Explain what Keely did wrong. Write the number correctly in scientific notation.
12. According to most-expensive.net, *Spider-Man 3* cost more to produce than any other movie before it. The budget was $258,000,000. Write this number in scientific notation.

EVALUATING EXPRESSIONS

LESSON 2

Evaluate expressions.

An expression that contains numbers, operations and variables is an **algebraic expression**. Variables are symbols used to represent numbers in algebraic expressions and equations. Algebraic expressions can be evaluated when the values of the variables are given.

EVALUATING EXPRESSIONS

1. Rewrite the expression by replacing the variables with the given values.
2. Follow the order of operations to compute the value of the expression.

EXAMPLE 1

Evaluate each algebraic expression.

a. $2x - 8$ when $x = 4$

b. $\dfrac{-5(m + y)}{m}$ when $m = -2$ and $y = 10$

SOLUTIONS

a. Write the expression. $\qquad$ $2x - 8$
   Substitute 4 for x. $\qquad$ $2(4) - 8$
   Multiply. $\qquad$ $8 - 8$
   Subtract. $\qquad$ 0

b. Write the expression. $\qquad$ $\dfrac{-5(m + y)}{m}$

   Substitute -2 for m and 10 for y. $\qquad$ $\dfrac{-5(-2 + 10)}{-2}$

   Add inside parentheses. $\qquad$ $\dfrac{-5(8)}{-2}$

   Multiply. $\qquad$ $\dfrac{-40}{-2}$

   Divide the numerator by the denominator. $\qquad$ 20

Input, x	$\dfrac{4 + 5x}{2}$	Output
2	$\dfrac{4 + 5(2)}{2}$	7
5	$\dfrac{4 + 5(5)}{2}$	14.5
−6	$\dfrac{4 + 5(-6)}{2}$	−13

Different values can be substituted for the variable in an expression. A table is used to help organize mathematical computations. The values for the variable are often called the input values. The values of the expression are often called the output values.

EXAMPLE 2 | **Fill in the table by evaluting the given expresson for the values listed.**

x	$-3x + 7$	Output
-2		
0		
4		
9		

SOLUTION

Rewrite the expression with the input value in the place of x and then follow the order of operations. In this case, multiply and then add to find the output values.

x	$-3x + 7$	Output
-2	$-3(-2) + 7$	13
0	$-3(0) + 7$	7
4	$-3(4) + 7$	-5
9	$-3(9) + 7$	-20

An **equation** is a mathematical sentence that contains an equals sign betweeen two expressions. Equations that involve at least one variable are neither true nor false until the equation is evaluated with given values for the variables. Values can be considered the solutions to an equation if they make the equation true.

EXAMPLE 3 | **State whether each equation is true or false for the values of the variables given.**
a. $3x + 2y = 8$ when $x = 2$ and $y = 1$
b. $-5x + 9 = y$ when $x = 6$ and $y = -21$
c. $y = \frac{1}{2}x + 1$ when $x = 8$ and $y = 17$

SOLUTIONS

a. Substitute $x = 2$ and $y = 1$. $3(2) + 2(1) \stackrel{?}{=} 8$
   Multiply. $6 + 2 \stackrel{?}{=} 8$
   Add. $8 = 8$ **TRUE**

b. Substitute $x = 6$ and $y = -21$. $-5(6) + 9 \stackrel{?}{=} -21$
   Multiply. $-30 + 9 \stackrel{?}{=} -21$
   Add. $-21 = -21$ **TRUE**

c. Substitute $x = 8$ and $y = 17$. $17 \stackrel{?}{=} \frac{1}{2}(8) + 1$
   Multiply. $17 \stackrel{?}{=} 4 + 1$
   Add. $17 \neq 5$ **FALSE**

EXERCISES

Evaluate each expression when $x = 3$.

1. $2x - 1$

2. $\dfrac{-9x + 5}{2}$

3. $\dfrac{1}{3}x - 7$

4. $(x + 3)^2$

5. $5(x - 1)^2 + 2$

6. $-9 - 5x$

Evaluate each expression for the given values of the variables.

7. $\dfrac{3x - 5}{2}$ when $x = 7$

8. $\dfrac{-2(7x - 3)}{5}$ when $x = 4$

9. $8y - 2x$ when $y = 5$ and $x = 5$

10. $\dfrac{3}{4}a + 3$ when $a = 12$

11. $(4 + 3x)^2$ when $x = -1$

12. $-3y + -4m$ when $y = 1$ and $m = \dfrac{1}{2}$

13. $y + \dfrac{x - 7}{5}$ when $y = -2$ and $x = 22$

14. $0.5m - 0.1n$ when $m = 10$ and $n = 10$

Copy each table. Complete each table by evaluating the given expression for the values listed.

15.

x	$6x - 4$	Output
-2		
0		
$\dfrac{1}{2}$		
3		
8		

16.

x	$\dfrac{5x - 3}{2}$	Output
-3		
0		
4		
11		

State whether each equation is true or false for the values of the variables given.

17. $5x + 2y = 10$ when $x = 2$ and $y = 0$

18. $-3x + y = 7$ when $x = 1$ and $y = 4$

19. $y = 8x + 9$ when $x = 5$ and $y = 40$

20. $4y = x + 5$ when $x = 7$ and $y = 3$

21. $y = 3(x - 6)$ when $x = 4$ and $y = -6$

22. $0.5x + 5y = 17.5$ when $x = 5$ and $y = 4$

23. $-3y + -4x = 20$ when $x = 0$ and $y = -5$

24. $\dfrac{1}{2}x + \dfrac{1}{2}y = 4$ when $x = 2$ and $y = 8$

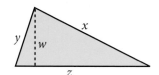 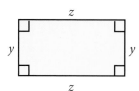 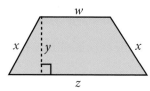

25. Use the formulas given to find the perimeter of each figure above when $w = 2$, $x = 5$, $y = 3$ and $z = 10$.

    a. TRIANGLE   **b.** RECTANGLE   **c.** TRAPEZOID
       $P = x + y + z$ $P = 2(y + z)$ $P = w + 2x + z$

26. Use the formulas given to find the area of each figure above when $w = 2$, $x = 5$, $y = 3$ and $z = 10$.

    a. TRIANGLE   **b.** RECTANGLE   **c.** TRAPEZOID
       $A = \frac{1}{2}wz$ $A = yz$ $A = \frac{1}{2}y(w + z)$

27. Tom went shopping at the mall. He found one type of shirt he liked for $12. He also discovered a pair of shorts for $16. Both the shirt and the shorts came in many different colors.

    a. Let x represent the number of shirts and y represent the number of shorts Tom purchases. Write an algebraic expression that represents the total cost for x shirts and y shorts.

    b. Tom decides to buy three shirts and five pairs of shorts. What is the total cost for this purchase?

    c. Sam, a friend of Tom's, decides to buy the same kind of shorts and shirts. His total cost for his purchase was $80. How many shirts and pairs of shorts do you think he purchased?

28. The table at right shows admission prices for Centerville's movie theater.

    a. The Johnson family consists of 2 adults, 1 senior citizen and three children (ages 3, 7 and 13). What will be the total cost for admission for the Johnson family to see a movie at the theater?

    b. Jacob is having a birthday bash for his thirteenth birthday. His mom agreed to take Jacob and 9 of his friends to the theater for the party. All of Jacob's friends are also twelve or thirteen. How much will it cost for all the kids plus Jacob's mom to go to the movie?

    c. Derrick spent $26.50 on movie admissions for his family. Give one possible description of the ages of people in Derrick's family.

Centerville Movie Admission

Adult (18-61 years old)	$8.00
Senior Citizen (62 years and above)	$6.50
Children (5-17 years old)	$4.00
Children (4 years and under)	$2.50

REVIEW

Evaluate each expression.

29. $5 + 2 \cdot 7 - 20$

30. $\frac{6 + 9}{3} + 4$

31. $1 - 10 + -11 + 2 \cdot 3^2$

32. $3(2 + 4)^2 - 100$

33. $-5 \cdot 7 + 6(-2 - 1)$

34. $\frac{70 - 10}{6 + 4} - 6$

THE DISTRIBUTIVE PROPERTY

LESSON 3

Simplify expressions using the Distributive Property and combining like terms.

Every algebraic expression has at least one term. A **term** is a number or the product of a number and a variable. Terms are separated by addition and subtraction signs. A **constant** is a term that has no variable. The number multiplied by a variable in a term is called the **coefficient**.

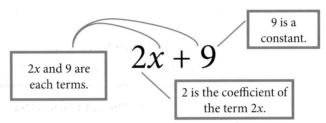

$$2x + 9$$

9 is a constant.

2x and 9 are each terms.

2 is the coefficient of the term 2x.

Some expressions contain parentheses. One tool that will help you work with these expressions is called the Distributive Property. The Distributive Property allows you to rewrite an expression without parentheses. This is done by distributing the front coefficient to each term inside the parentheses. This will be a crucial step in solving equations that contain parentheses.

THE DISTRIBUTIVE PROPERTY

For any numbers a, b and c:

$$a(b + c) = a \cdot b + a \cdot c$$
$$a(b - c) = a \cdot b - a \cdot c$$

EXAMPLE 1

Use the Distributive Property to simplify each expression.
a. $2(x + 6)$ **b.** $\frac{1}{4}(y - 20)$ **c.** $-5(3x - 1)$

SOLUTIONS

Drawing arrows from the front coefficient to each term inside the parentheses will help guide you.

a. $2(x + 6)$ $= 2(x) + 2(6)$
                      $= 2x + 12$

b. $\frac{1}{4}(y - 20)$ $= \frac{1}{4}(y) - \frac{1}{4}(20)$
                                 $= \frac{1}{4}y - 5$

Watch the signs when distributing a negative number.

c. $-5(3x - 1)$ $= -5(3x) - (-5)(1)$
                        $= -15x + 5$

X2313006006139

Lesson 3 ~ The Distributive Property **11**

The Distributive Property is very useful when doing mental math calculations. Certain numbers are easier to multiply together than others. In **Example 2**, notice how you can rewrite a number as a sum or difference of two other numbers that are easier to work with and then do the math mentally.

EXAMPLE 2

Find each product by using the Distributive Property and mental math.

a. $4(103)$ **b.** $998 \cdot 7$ **c.** $8(6.5)$

SOLUTIONS

a. $4(103) = 4(100 + 3)$
$4(100) + 4(3)$
$400 + 12 = 412$

b. $998 \cdot 7 = 7(1000 - 2)$
$7(1000) - 7(2)$
$7000 - 14 = 6{,}986$

c. $8(6.5) = 8(6 + 0.5)$
$8(6) + 8(0.5)$
$48 + 4 = 52$

An algebraic expression or equation may have like terms that can be combined. Like terms are terms that have the same variable raised to the same power. The numerical coefficients do not need to be the same. If there are parentheses involved in the expression, the Distributive Property must be used FIRST before combining like terms.

An expression is simplified if it has no parentheses and all like terms have been combined. When combining like terms you must remember that the operation in front of the term (addition or subtraction) must remain attached to the term. Rewrite the expression by grouping like terms together before adding or subtracting the coefficients to simplify.

EXAMPLE 3

Simplify by combining like terms. $3x - 2y + 4 - 2x + x + 4y$

SOLUTION

Mark terms that are alike. $3x - 2y + 4 - 2x + x + 4y$

Group like terms. $3x - 2x + x \quad -2y + 4y \ + 4$

Combine. $2x + 2y + 4$

> A subtraction sign is treated as a negative sign on the coefficient it precedes.

EXAMPLE 4

Simplify by combining like terms. $-5(2x - 1) + 3x - 2$

SOLUTION

Distribute. $-5(2x - 1) + 3x - 2 \quad = -10x + 5 + 3x - 2$

Group like terms. $= -10x + 3x + 5 - 2$

Combine. $= -7x + 3$

In each example so far in this lesson, the original and simplified expressions are called equivalent expressions. Two or more expressions that represent the same simplified algebraic expression are called equivalent expressions.

Step 1: On your own paper, copy each expression below. Leave at least two lines between each expression.

      A. $2(x + 4) - 5$ **F.** $20 - 3(x + 4) - 2x$

      B. $3(x - 3) - 2x$ **G.** $3x + 3 + 7x - 8x$

      C. $1 + 8(x + 1)$ **H.** $-2(x - 3) + x + 5$

      D. $9 - 4x - 1 - x$ **I.** $2(x + 7) - 3(x + 1)$

      E. $2(4x - 5) + 1 - 7x$ **J.** $6x + 5x - x - 2x + 9$

Step 2: Simplify each expression.

Step 3: Every expression listed above is equivalent to one other expression in the list. Classify the ten expressions into five groups of equivalent expressions.

Step 4: Create another 'non-simplified' expression for each group that is equivalent to the other expressions in the group.

EXERCISES

Use the Distributive Property to simplify each expression.

1. $5(x + 1)$ **2.** $\frac{3}{5}(5x + 10)$ **3.** $2(4m + 5)$

4. $-6(x - 10)$ **5.** $-3(h - 11)$ **6.** $16\left(\frac{1}{2}x - 2\right)$

Find the product by using the Distributive Property.

7. $7(105)$ **8.** $68(10.5)$

9. $896 \cdot 4$ **10.** $6(999)$

11. Tasha finds 7 DVDs she wants to purchase at the video store. Each DVD is $14.95.
    a. Show how Tasha could use the distributive property to help mentally calculate the total cost of the DVDs.
    b. How much will she pay for the seven DVDs?

Simplify each expression.

12. $9 + 2x - 4 + 8x$

13. $7(x - 2) + 6(x + 1)$

14. $7 + 3(x - 4)$

15. $-9x + 8x + 7y - 6y$

16. $7x + 3y - x + 4y - 2x$

17. $12y - 3x + 10x - y$

18. $-10(3x + 2) - 12$

19. $9x - 3(x + 2) + 7$

Write and simplify an expression for the perimeter of each figure.

20.
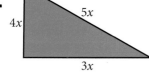

21.
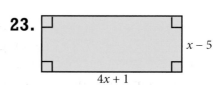

22.
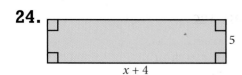

23.
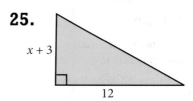

Write and simplify an expression for the area of each figure.

Area of Rectangle = *length · width*   Area of Triangle = $\frac{1}{2}$*base · height*

24.
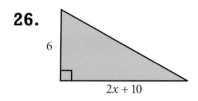

25.

26.
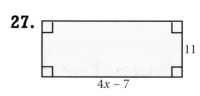

27.

In each set of three expressions, two are equivalent. Simplify each expression to find the equivalent expressions.

28. A. $3x + 4 - 2 + 7x$

   B. $18x - 5 - 8x + 7$

   C. $2x + 8x - 4 + 2$

29. A. $3(x - 1) + 12$

   B. $4(x + 3) - 1$

   C. $4(x + 2) - x + 1$

30. Whitney states that $8x - 7$ is equivalent to $7 - 8x$. Do you agree with her? Explain your answer.

31. Evaluate each expression when $x = 2$.

    a. $5(x + 8)$ **b.** $\dfrac{3x - 2}{6}$

    c. $(x + 5)^2 + 2x$ **d.** $16\left(\frac{1}{2}x + 1\right)$

32. Francis earns \$20 per day for yard work plus \$4 more for every pound of yard debris she removes.

    a. Write an expression that represents the total amount Francis would be paid for a day of yard work when she disposed of x pounds of yard debris.

    b. Calculate how much Francis would get paid on a day when she removed 18 pounds of yard debris.

TIC-TAC-TOE ~ ORDER OF OPS POETRY

Poetry is an art form that is composed of carefully chosen words to express a greater depth of meaning. Poetry can be written about many different subjects, including mathematics. The order of operations is a key element in mathematics so that all students, teachers and mathematicians reach the same answer when calculating the value of the same expression. Write two different poems about the order of operations. One should be an acrostic poem and the other should be a quatrain. Research and find another style of poetry. Write one more poem about the order of operations using this style.

Quatrain

A poem consisting of four lines. Lines 2 and 4 must rhyme and have a similar number of syllables.

Acrostic

A poem where certain letters, usually the first in each line, form a word or message when read in a sequence.

TIC-TAC-TOE ~ LIKE TERMS GAME

Write 15 variable expressions containing like terms that have not been combined. Make sure you have a minimum of five expressions containing parentheses. Cut thicker paper (such as cardstock, construction paper, index cards or poster board) into 30 equal-sized pieces. Write each expression on one card. On another card, write the expression in simplest form. Use these cards to play a memory game with a friend, classmate or family member. Record each pair of cards each participant wins on a sheet of paper by listing the non-simplified and simplified expressions. Turn in the cards and the game sheet to your teacher.

SOLVING ONE - STEP EQUATIONS

Use inverse operations to solve one-step equations.

In order to solve a mathematical equation, the variable must be isolated on one side of the equation and have a front coefficient of one. This process is sometimes referred to as "getting the variable by itself". The most important thing to remember is that the equation must always remain balanced. Whatever occurs on one side of the equals sign MUST occur on the other side so the equation remains balanced. The properties of equality are listed below. Note that you can perform any of the four basic operations to an equation as long as that operation is done to both sides of the equation.

THE PROPERTIES OF EQUALITY

For any numbers a, b and c:

If $a = b$, then $a + c = b + c$ (Addition Property of Equality)

If $a = b$, then $a - c = b - c$ (Subtraction Property of Equality)

If $a = b$, then $a \cdot c = b \cdot c$ (Multiplication Property of Equality)

If $a = b$, then $\frac{a}{c} = \frac{b}{c}$ (Division Property of Equality)

EXPLORE!   **ADDITION AND SUBTRACTION EQUATIONS**

Each blue chip represents the integer +1. Each red chip represents the integer −1. When a positive integer chip is combined with a negative integer chip, the result is zero. This pair of integer chips is called a zero pair.

Step 1: On your equation mat, place the variable cube on one side with 4 positive integer chips. On the other side of the mat, place 9 positive integer chips. Write the equation that is represented by the items on the mat.

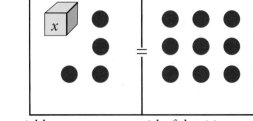

Step 2: In order to isolate the variable, you must get rid of the 4 integer chips with the variable. If you take chips off one side of the equation, you must do the same on the other side. How many chips are left on the right side? What does this represent?

Step 3: Clear your mat and place chips on the mat to represent the equation $x - 2 = 6$. Draw this on a sheet of paper.

Step 4: How could you "get rid of" the chips that are with the variable? How many chips end up on the opposite side of the mat when you cancel out the 2 negative integer chips that are with the variable? Write your answer in the form $x = $ ___.

Step 5: Clear your mat and place chips on the mat to represent the equation $-3 + x = -1$. Draw this on your own paper.

Step 6: Isolate the variable by canceling out chips on the variable side of the equation. Remember that whatever you do to one side of the equation you must do to the other side. What does x equal in this case?

Step 7: Create your own equation on your mat. Record the algebraic equation on your paper.

Step 8: Solve your equation. What does your variable equal?

Step 9: Write a few sentences that describe how to solve a one-step addition or subtraction equation using equation mats, integer counters and variable cubes.

You will not always have integer chips or an equation mat available to use when you are solving equations. You can solve equations using the balancing method on paper. When isolating the variable, remember to perform an **inverse operation** on both sides of the equation. Inverse operations are operations that undo each other, such as addition and subtraction.

EXAMPLE 1

Solve for x. Check your solution.

a. $x - 6 = 22$ b. $8x = 88$

c. $x + 10 = -7$ d. $\dfrac{x}{5} = 21$

SOLUTIONS

Draw a vertical line through the equals sign to help you stay organized. Whatever is done on one side of the line to cancel out a value must be done on the other side.

a. $x - 6 = 22$
$\underline{+6 \quad +6}$
$\boxed{x = 28}$

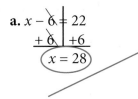
Check the answer by substituting the answer back into the equation.

$\checkmark$ $28 - 6 \overset{?}{=} 22$
$22 = 22$

b. $\dfrac{8x}{8} = \dfrac{88}{8}$
$\boxed{x = 11}$

$\checkmark$ $8(11) \overset{?}{=} 88$
$88 = 88$

c. $x + 10 = -7$
$\underline{-10 \quad -10}$
$\boxed{x = -17}$

$\checkmark$ $-17 + 10 \overset{?}{=} -7$
$-7 = -7$

d. $5 \cdot \dfrac{x}{5} = 21 \cdot 5$
$\boxed{x = 105}$

$\checkmark$ $\dfrac{105}{5} \overset{?}{=} 21$

$21 = 21$

Equations in this lesson have been written symbolically. There will be times when an equation will be written in words and need to be translated into mathematical symbols in order to solve the equation. Here are some key words you need to remember when translating words into math symbols:

Addition	Subtraction	Multiplication	Division	Equals
sum increased by more than plus	difference decreased by less than minus	product multiplied by times of	quotient divided by	is equal to is

EXAMPLE 2

Write an equation for each statement. Solve each equation and check your solution.
a. The product of eleven and a number is seventy-seven.
b. The sum of a number and 52 is 98.
c. A number decreased by 13 is 214.

SOLUTIONS

a. Write the equation. "Product" means multiplication.
Divide both sides of the equation by 11.
The number is 7.

$$11x = 77$$
$$\frac{\cancel{11}x}{\cancel{11}} = \frac{77}{11}$$
$$\boxed{x = 7}$$

☑ Check the answer.

$$11 \cdot 7 = 77$$

b. Write the equation. "Sum" means addition.

Subtract 52 from both sides of the equation.
The number is 46.

$$p + 52 = 98$$
$$\begin{array}{r} p + 52 = 98 \\ -52 \quad -52 \\ \hline \end{array}$$
$$\boxed{p = 46}$$

☑ Check the answer.

$$46 + 52 = 98$$

c. Write the equation. "Decreased by" means subtraction.

Add 13 to both sides of the equation.
The number is 227.

$$y - 13 = 214$$
$$\begin{array}{r} y - 13 = 214 \\ +13 \quad +13 \\ \hline \end{array}$$
$$\boxed{y = 227}$$

☑ Check the answer.

$$227 - 13 = 214$$

EXAMPLE 3

The sum of Kirk's age and his dad's age is 53. Kirk is 14. Write an equation that represents this situation using _d_ to represent the dad's age. Solve the equation and check your solution.

SOLUTION

Write the equation.
Subtract 14 from both sides of the equation.

$$\begin{array}{r} 14 + d = 53 \\ -14 \quad -14 \\ \hline d = 39 \end{array}$$

☑ Check the answer.

$$14 + 39 = 53$$

Kirk's dad is 39 years old.

EXERCISES

Solve each equation for *x*. Check your solution.

1. $x - 4 = 27$

2. $-4x = 84$

3. $6x = 54$

4. $-12 + x = -30$

5. $96 = 35 + x$

6. $\frac{x}{5} = 8$

7. $\frac{x}{6} = -12$

8. $x - 3 = -9$

9. $-110 = -5x$

10. Shawn did not check his solutions for the four-problem quiz on one-step equations.
Check Shawn's answers. If the answer is incorrect, find the correct answer.

    a. $x + 82 = 124$
       Shawn's answer: $x = 206$

    b. $-7 + x = 12$
       Shawn's answer: $x = 19$

    c. $9x = 63$
       Shawn's answer: $x = -7$

    d. $\frac{x}{4} = 8$
       Shawn's answer: $x = 2$

11. Patty wants to use an equation mat, integer chips and variable cubes to illustrate a one-step multiplication equation. On a separate piece of paper, draw a picture of how she could illustrate the equation $3x = 12$ on the mat. Illustrate how the integer chips can be separated into three equal parts on the mat to show the solution to the equation. State the value of *x*.

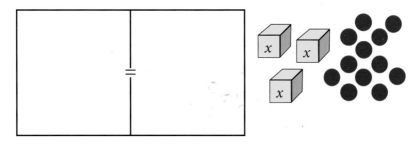

Write an equation for each statement and solve for the variable. Check your solution.

12. The product of 8 and a number is 48.

13. The sum of a number and −53 is 89.

14. A number divided by −7 is −7.

15. Sixteen less than a number is 102.

16. A number increased by $1\frac{1}{2}$ is $2\frac{3}{4}$.

17. One-third of a number is 6.

18. Mike is thinking of two numbers. Their difference is 12. If one of the numbers is 19, what is the other number? Is there only one answer? If not, what is the other possibility for the second number?

19. It is a common belief that one human year is equal to 7 dog years.

   a. Write an expression that will calculate how old a dog is in dog years based on it's normal "human year" age. Use x to represent the number of human years.

   b. If a dog is 84 dog years old when he passes away, how old was he in human years? Write an equation to represent this situation and solve the equation.

Solve each equation for x. Check the solution.

20. $x + 1.73 = 2.81$

21. $-0.1x = 16$

22. $\frac{2}{3}x = 10$

23. $\frac{6}{11}x = \frac{21}{22}$

24. $-2.5 + x = 6.75$

25. $-x = 3.4$

REVIEW

Evaluate each expression.

26. $12 + 12 \div 3 \cdot 5 - 1$

27. $\frac{(3 + 7)^2}{5} + 6$

28. $3(-21 + 10) + 7$

29. $-4\left(\frac{1}{2} + \frac{1}{2}\right) - 2$

Use the Distributive Property to simplify each expression.

30. $6(x - 3)$

31. $-2(9x - 1)$

32. $-4(5m + 7)$

33. $\frac{1}{4}(8x - 4)$

34. Evaluate the following using mental math.

   a. $-3 + -2$ **b.** $-4(6)$ **c.** $-5 + 11$ **d.** $6 - 9$

   e. $27 \div 3$ **f.** $(-20)(-5)$ **g.** $-8 + 1$ **h.** $\frac{-36}{6}$

SOLVING TWO - STEP EQUATIONS

 Solve two-step equations.

J im took a summer road trip across the country. He started his trip 20 miles east of Portland. He headed east on I-84. Every hour (h) he traveled 60 miles further away from Portland. The expression that represents his distance from Portland is:

$$d = 20 + 60h$$

Jim forgot to bring a watch, but noticed that he was 500 miles from Portland after his first day of driving. Assuming Jim traveled at an equal rate, how many hours did Jim drive on the first day of his road trip?

To solve this problem, you must be able to solve a two-step equation. Since Jim has driven 500 miles, substitute that value for d in the equation:

$$500 = 20 + 60h$$

To isolate the variable in a two-step equation you must perform two inverse operations. The inverse operations must undo the order of operations. That means you start by undoing addition or subtraction. Then use inverse operations to remove any multiplication or division.

How long has Jim been on the road?

Write an equation.
Subtract 20 from both sides of the equation.
Divide both sides of the equation by 60.

$$
\begin{array}{r}
500 = 20 + 60h \\
\underline{-20 \quad -20} \\
\dfrac{480}{60} = \dfrac{60h}{60}
\end{array}
$$

$$\boxed{8 = h}$$

Jim has been on his road trip for 8 hours.

EXAMPLE 1	**Solve the equation for x. Check the solution.** $8x - 3 = 85$

SOLUTION

Add 3 to both sides of the equation.

$$
\begin{array}{r}
8x - 3 = 85 \\
\underline{+3 \quad +3}
\end{array}
$$

Divide both sides of the equation by 8.

$$\dfrac{8x}{8} = \dfrac{88}{8}$$

$$\boxed{x = 11}$$

☑ Check the answer.

$$8(11) - 3 \overset{?}{=} 85$$
$$88 - 3 \overset{?}{=} 85$$
$$85 = 85$$

EXAMPLE 2

SOLUTION

Solve the equation for *x*. Check the solution. $-2 = \dfrac{x}{9} + 5$

> The variable can be on either side of the equals sign.

Subtract 5 from both sides of the equation.

$$-2 = \dfrac{x}{9} + 5$$
$$\underline{-5 \qquad\qquad -5}$$

Multiply both sides of the equation by 9.

$$9 \cdot (-7) = \dfrac{x}{9} \cdot 9$$

$$\boxed{-63 = x}$$

☑ Check the solution.

$$-2 \overset{?}{=} \dfrac{-63}{9} + 5$$
$$-2 \overset{?}{=} -7 + 5$$
$$-2 = -2$$

EXAMPLE 3

SOLUTION

Use an equation mat to illustrate and solve the equation $2x - 4 = 6$.

Lay out the variable cubes and integer chips to match the equation.

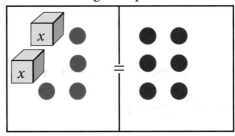

Remove the integer chips from the side with the variable by canceling out four negative integer chips with four positive integer chips (add 4 positive chips to each side).

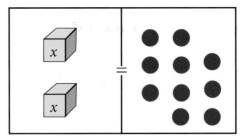

Divide the integer chips on the right side of the mat equally between the two cubes.

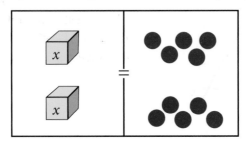

Write the solution. $x = 5$

EXAMPLE 4

Eight more than 3 times a number is 29. Write and solve an equation to find the value of the number.

SOLUTION

Write the equation.

Three times a number $3x$

Eight more than $3x + 8$

Is 29 $3x + 8 = 29$

> The word 'is' often means = in math.

$$3x + 8 = 29$$
$$\underline{-8 \quad -8}$$
$$\frac{3x}{3} = \frac{21}{3}$$
$$\boxed{x = 7}$$

☑ Check the solution.

$$3(7) + 8 \overset{?}{=} 29$$
$$21 + 8 \overset{?}{=} 29$$
$$29 = 29$$

EXERCISES

Solve each equation for x. Check the solution.

1. $4x + 2 = 18$

2. $\frac{x}{3} - 4 = 26$

3. $\frac{x}{5} - 7 = 3$

4. $102 = 20x - 8$

5. $-8 + 10x = 102$

6. $\frac{1}{2}x + \frac{3}{4} = 1$

7. $-18 = \frac{x}{3} + 2$

8. $2.5x + 7.5 = 20$

9. $32 = -8 + 4x$

10. The Fahrenheit and Celsius scales are related by the equation:
$$F = \frac{9}{5}C + 32$$

    a. The lowest temperature in Alaska, −62° C, was recorded on January 23, 1971 at Prospect Creek Camp. Use the formula to convert the record temperature to Fahrenheit.

    b. In February, the average high temperature in Puerto Vallarta, Mexico is 81° F. Use the formula to convert the average temperature to Celsius.

11. Jordin solved three problems incorrectly. Describe the error she made in each problem; then find the correct answers.

a.

$$3x - 6 \neq 27$$
$$\underline{-6 \quad | \quad -6}$$
$$\frac{3x}{3} \neq \frac{21}{3}$$

$$x = 7$$

b.

$$45 \neq 10x + 15$$
$$\underline{-15 \quad -15}$$
$$\frac{45}{-5} \neq \frac{-5x}{-5}$$

$$x = -9$$

c.

$$\frac{x}{8} - 2 \neq 22$$
$$\underline{+2 \quad | \quad +2}$$
$$8 \div \frac{x}{8} \neq 24 \div 8$$

$$x = 3$$

Write an equation for each statement. Solve each equation and check the solution.

12. Seven more than twice a number is 25.

13. Six less than the quotient of a number and 3 is −1.

14. Twelve decreased by 5 times a number is 72.

15. Four more than one-half a number is 3.

16. Barry begins the year with $25 in his piggy bank. At the end of each month, Barry adds $3.
   a. How much will Barry have after 5 months have passed?
   b. Write a formula that could be used to calculate Barry's total savings (S) based on how many months (m) he has deposited money in his bank.
   c. Use your formula to determine how many months have passed when Barry reaches $100 in his account.

17. Mariah's parents got into a car accident. They took their car to the shop to be repaired. When the car was finished, they received a bill of $637. The total cost for parts was $280 and the cost of labor was $42 per hour. Determine how many hours the mechanics spent working on the car. Explain in words how you found your answer.

18. Ryan sells cars for a living. He gets paid $50 per day plus a commission of 2% of the total cost of each car he sells. Ryan's daily earnings (E) can be represented by the equation $E = 0.02x + 50$ where x is the amount of his sales for the day.
   a. What does the 0.02 represent in the equation?
   b. How much did Ryan make on Monday if he only sold one car for $4,400?
   c. Ryan wants to make $1,000 in a day. What must his daily sales be to reach this goal?

Copy each line and insert any combination of the four operations (+, −, ×, ÷) to make each statement true.

19. 2   3   5 = 17

20. 12   6   10 = −8

21. −1   2   2 = 0

22. 20   5   50   5 = 45

Simplify each expression.

23. $9(x − 2)$

24. $−7 + 6(x − 5) + 2x$

25. $2x + 4x + 7x − 3x$

26. $2(x − 1) + 3(x + 1)$

27. $4(x + 8) − 12$

28. $−5(x + 3) + 5x + 13$

TIC-TAC-TOE ~ TEMPERATURE SYSTEMS

There are three common units of temperatures:
Fahrenheit, Kelvin and Celsius.

1. Research the three common units of temperature. Where was each one invented? Where is each one most often used? How are the units related to each other? The following relationships are used to convert one unit of temperature to another:

$$F = 1.8C + 32 \qquad K = C + 273.15$$

2. Convert the following units from one system to another.
    a. 20° C to Fahrenheit   **b.** 20° C to Kelvin
    c. 78º F to Celsius   **d.** 289.5 K to Celsius
    e. −4° F to Celsius   **f.** 315 K to Fahrenheit

3. Develop an equation that will convert Fahrenheit to Kelvin.

TIC-TAC-TOE ~ WHAT'S THE PROCESS?

Solving a multi-step equation can be a complicated task depending on the difficulty of the equation. Create a poster to help classmates through the process step-by-step. Include at least two examples on your poster. Address what a student should do if the following items show up in their equation:

◆ Multiplication or Division
◆ Addition or Subtraction
◆ Variables on Different Sides of the Equals Sign
◆ Variables on the Same Side of the Equals Sign
◆ Parentheses

Lesson 5 ~ Solving Two - Step Equations **25**

SOLVING MULTI - STEP EQUATIONS

 Simplify and solve multi-step equations.

Two different stores at the beach rent bicycles. One store charges an initial fee of $4 plus $2 per hour. This can be represented by the expression $4 + 2h$ when h is the number of hours the bike is rented. The other store charges an initial fee of $10 but only charges $0.50 per hour. This situation is represented by the expression $10 + 0.5h$ when h is the number of hours the bike is rented. At what point would the two bike rentals cost the exact same amount?

The times would be the same when the two expressions are equal.
$$4 + 2h = 10 + 0.5h$$

To solve this equation, you must first get the variables on the same side of the equation. To do this, move one variable term to the opposite side of the equation using inverse operations. It is easiest to move the variable term with the smaller coefficient. This often helps you deal with fewer negative numbers. After the variables are on the same side of the equation, solve the two-step equation that remains.

Subtract $0.5h$ from both sides of the equation.

$$
\begin{array}{r}
4 + 2h = 10 + 0.5h \\
-0.5h \qquad -0.5h \\
\hline
4 + 1.5h = 10 \\
-4 \qquad\quad -4 \\
\hline
\dfrac{1.5h}{1.5} = \dfrac{6}{1.5} \\
\end{array}
$$

Subtract 4 from both sides of the equation.
Divide both sides of the equation by 1.5.

$$\boxed{h = 4}$$

The two bike rentals cost the same amount at 4 hours.

To check the solution, substitute the value into each side of the equation. If both sides are equal, the solution is correct.

First store for 4 hours: ☑ $4 + 2(4) = \$12$
Second store for 4 hours: ☑ $10 + 0.5(4) = \$12$

SOLVING MULTI-STEP EQUATIONS

1. Simplify each side of the equation by distributing and combining like terms, when necessary.
2. If variables are on both sides of the equation, balance the equation by moving one variable term to the opposite side of the equals sign using inverse operations.
3. Follow the process for solving one- and two-step equations to get the variable by itself.

Step 1: Write the equation that is represented by the equation mat shown below.

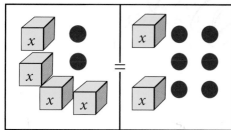

Step 2: There are variable cubes on both sides of the mat. Remove the same number of cubes from each side so that only one side has variable cubes remaining. Draw a picture of what is on the mat now.

Step 3: What is the next step you must take to balance the equation mat? Remember that your goal is to isolate the variable. Draw a picture of what is on the mat now.

Step 4: Once the variables are isolated, x can be determined by dividing the integer chips on the opposite side equally between the remaining variable cubes. How many integer chips belong to each variable cube? What does this represent?

Step 5: Draw a representation of $5x + 7 = 2x + 4$ on an equation mat.

Step 6: Repeat **Steps 2 - 4**. What is the solution to this equation?

EXAMPLE 1

Solve the equation for x. $4(2x - 7) = 20$

SOLUTION

Distribute.

Add 28 to both sides of the equation.

Divide both sides of the equation by 8.

$$4(2x - 7) = 20$$
$$8x - 28 = 20$$
$$\underline{+\ 28\ \ \ \ +28}$$
$$\frac{8x}{8} = \frac{48}{8}$$
$$\boxed{x = 6}$$

☑ Check the solution.

$$4(2 \cdot 6 - 7) \overset{?}{=} 20$$
$$4(12 - 7) \overset{?}{=} 20$$
$$4(5) \overset{?}{=} 20$$
$$20 = 20$$

EXAMPLE 2

Solve the equation for x. $\quad -2x + 9 = 4x - 15$

SOLUTION

There are no parentheses so there is no need to use the Distributive Property.

Add $2x$ to both sides of the equation.

Add 15 to both sides of the equation.

Divide both sides of the equation by 6.

$$
\begin{array}{r}
-2x + 9 = 4x - 15 \\
\underline{+2x \qquad +2x} \\
9 = 6x - 15 \\
\underline{+15 \qquad +15} \\
\dfrac{24}{6} = \dfrac{6x}{6} \\
\boxed{4 = x}
\end{array}
$$

☑ Check the solution.

$$
\begin{array}{c}
-2(4) + 9 \stackrel{?}{=} 4(4) - 15 \\
-8 + 9 \stackrel{?}{=} 16 - 15 \\
1 = 1
\end{array}
$$

EXAMPLE 3

Solve the equation for x. $\quad 5(x + 8) = -2(x - 13)$

SOLUTION

Use the Distributive Property to remove the parentheses.

Add $2x$ to both sides of the equation.

Subtract 40 from both sides of the equation.

Divide both sides of the equation by 7.

$$
\begin{array}{r}
5(x + 8) = -2(x - 13) \\
5x + 40 = -2x + 26 \\
\underline{+2x \qquad +2x} \\
7x + 40 = 26 \\
\underline{-40 \qquad -40} \\
\dfrac{7x}{7} = \dfrac{-14}{7} \\
\boxed{x = -2}
\end{array}
$$

☑ Check the solution.

$$
\begin{array}{c}
5(-2 + 8) \stackrel{?}{=} -2(-2 - 13) \\
5(6) \stackrel{?}{=} -2(-15) \\
30 = 30
\end{array}
$$

EXAMPLE 4

Katie opened a coffee cart to earn some extra money. Her one-time equipment start-up cost was $460. It costs her $1 to make each cup of coffee. She plans to sell the cups of coffee for $3. How many cups will she need to sell before she breaks even?

SOLUTION

Let x represent the number of cups of coffee sold.

Write an equation that represents the situation.

$$460 + 1x = 3x$$

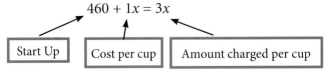

| Start Up | Cost per cup | Amount charged per cup |

EXAMPLE 4
SOLUTION
(CONTINUED)

Subtract $1x$ from both sides of the equation.

Divide both sides by 2.

$$
\begin{array}{r|r}
460 + 1x & 3x \\
-1x & -1x \\
\hline
460 & 2x \\
\hline
2 & 2
\end{array}
$$

$$\boxed{230 = x}$$

☑ Check the solution.

$$460 + 1(230) \stackrel{?}{=} 3(230)$$
$$460 + 230 \stackrel{?}{=} 690$$
$$690 = 690$$

Katie must sell 230 cups of coffee before she will break even.

EXERCISES

1. Draw an equation mat with integer chips and variable cubes that represents the equation $x + 9 = 3x + 1$. Describe in words or pictures how you would move items around on the mat to solve this equation. What is the solution to this equation?

Solve each equation. Check the solution.

2. $2(3x + 6) = 42$

3. $10x = 4x + 66$

4. $-3(x + 4) = -15$

5. $9x + 20 = 34 - 5x$

6. $5x + 3 - 2x = 3$

7. $\frac{1}{2}(6x - 8) = 41$

8. Explain the steps to finding the solution for a multi-step equation.

9. Kelsey made cupcakes to sell as a fundraiser for her trip to Washington DC. She purchased one cupcake pan for $12. She calculated that the ingredients cost her $0.25 per cupcake. She plans to sell the cupcakes for $0.75 each.
   a. Write an equation that could be used to find the number of cupcakes (x) she will need to sell to break even.
   b. Solve the equation from **part a**. Check the solution.
   c. If she sold 184 cupcakes, what was her profit?

Solve each equation. Check the solution.

10. $7x - 9 = -4x + 90$

11. $\frac{1}{4}x + 12 = \frac{1}{2}x + 10$

12. $3(x - 6) = 6x - 90$

13. $2x + 7x + 10 = 11x$

14. $6(x + 2) = 2(2x + 4)$

15. $4.6x - 8.5 = 1.3x + 1.4$

16. $5x = 10x - 4x + 7$

17. $3(2x - 5) = 2x + 1$

18. $x - \frac{1}{3} = 3x + \frac{2}{3}$

19. Francisco made only one mistake on his homework. Describe the mistake he made and solve the equation correctly.

$$3(x - 7) \neq 5x - 11$$
$$3x - 7 \neq 5x - 11$$
$$\underline{-3x \qquad -3x}$$
$$-7 \neq 2x - 11$$
$$\underline{+11 \qquad \quad +11}$$
$$\frac{4}{2} \neq \frac{2x}{2}$$
$$2 = x$$

20. An internet movie rental company has two different options for renting movies.

    a. Copy the table below and fill in the total amount paid for movies rented under each plan.

> Option A: Pay a one-time $40 membership fee and then pay $1 for each movie rental.
> Option B: Do not become a member and pay $6 for each movie rental.

Movies Rented	Total Cost Option A	Total Cost Option B
0	$40	$0
1		
2		
3		
4		
5		
6		
7		
8		
9		

    b. Write an expression to represent the total cost for **Option A**. Use x for the number of videos rented.
    c. Write an expression to represent the total cost for **Option B**. Use x for the number of videos rented.
    d. Set the two expressions equal to each other. Solve for x.
    e. Explain what the answer to **part d** means in real life. Does the table in **part a** support your answer?
    f. Sal thinks he will rent about 15 movies this year. Which plan would be a better deal for him? Why?

REVIEW

State whether each equation is true or false for the values of the variables given.

21. $5x - 2y = 10$ when $x = 2$ and $y = 0$

22. $4x + 1 = y$ when $x = 5$ and $y = 46$

23. $2(x + 3) = y$ when $x = 3$ and $y = 9$

24. $y = -4(x + 10)$ when $x = -6$ and $y = -16$

TIC-TAC-TOE ~ SMALL BUSINESS PROFITS

When someone opens a small business, they often use linear equations to determine profits and losses. Three individuals started up three different businesses which are described below.

Business #1
Sarah's Coffee Shop
Start-Up Cost = $275
Profit per Coffee Sold = $2.50
Linear Equation:
$P = -275 + 2.50C$

Business #2
Jason's Skateboarding Store
Start-Up Cost = $400
Profit per Board Sold = $14

Business #3
Jamal's Gaming Shop
Start-Up Cost = $750
Profit per Game Sold = $9.75

1. A linear equation representing total profits is shown for Business #1. Write the linear equations for the total profits for the other two businesses.

2. For each business, determine how many items they will need to sell to earn back the amount of money they spent for starting their business.

3. Each business has a goal of making a total profit of $10,000 in the first quarter of the year. Determine how many total items they will each need to sell to reach their goal.

4. Design your own small business.

    a. Choose one item to sell. Describe why you would like to sell this item.

    b. Estimate the total start-up costs. Explain how you came up with this amount.

    c. Estimate the total profit you hope to make per item sold. Explain how you came up with this amount.

    d. Repeat #1 - #3 above for your small business idea.

    e. Do you think there would be enough interest in your product to reach the goal of $10,000 in the first quarter? Explain.

TIC-TAC-TOE ~ EQUATION MATS

Equation mats are used to see a visual model of the equation-solving process. Write a "How To…" guide about using equation mats for different types of equations. Include the following types of equations in your guide:

    ♦ One-Step Equations

    ♦ Two-Step Equations

    ♦ Equations with Variables on Both Sides of the Equals Sign

THE COORDINATE PLANE AND SCATTER PLOTS

 Graph points on the coordinate plane.

The **coordinate plane** is created by drawing two number lines which intersect at a 90° angle. These two lines are called the **axes**. Each number line intersects the other at zero. The point where the two lines cross is called the **origin**. The horizontal axis is used for the variable *x* (called the *x*-axis) and the vertical axis is used for the variable *y* (called the *y*-axis). The axes divide the coordinate plane into four quadrants. The **quadrants** are numbered I, II, III and IV starting in the top right quadrant and moving counter-clockwise.

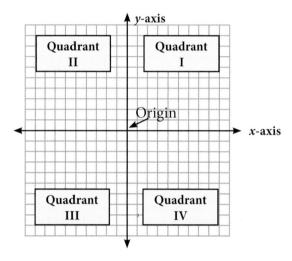

Each point on the graph is named by an **ordered pair**. The first number in the ordered pair corresponds to the numbers on the *x*-axis. The second number corresponds to the number on the *y*-axis.

EXAMPLE 1

Graph each point and name the quadrant where each point is located.
a. A(5, 6)   **c.** C(0, 3)
b. B(−4, 8)   **d.** D(9, −1)

SOLUTIONS

Quadrant Location
a. Quadrant I
b. Quadrant II
c. None (on the *y*-axis)
d. Quadrant IV

(5, 6) → Start at the origin and move right 5 units and up 6 units.

(−4, 8) → Start at the origin and move left 4 units and up 8 units.

(9, −1) → Start at the origin and move right 9 units and down 1 unit.

Xavier was babysitting his little sister, Sam, one afternoon. His sister wanted to do a connect-the-dots but Xavier could not find any in the house. He decided to create one for Sam to do. He recorded the ordered pairs that would need to be connected in the order he wanted Sam to connect them.

Step 1: Draw and label the *x*- and *y*-axis. Number each axis from −10 to 10.

Step 2: Plot Xavier's points and connect the points in the order they are listed.
Start at $(8, 0) \rightarrow (6, 2) \rightarrow (−2, 2) \rightarrow (−5, 5) \rightarrow (−5, −5) \rightarrow (−2, −2) \rightarrow (6, −2) \rightarrow (8, 0)$

Step 3: Is the picture recognizable? If so, what do you think it is?

Step 4: What are a few of the limitations of trying to draw a picture by connecting the dots on a coordinate plane?

Step 5: Create your own instructions for a connect-the-dots that uses at least eight points in at least three quadrants. List your points in the order they should be connected.

Step 6: Have a classmate try your connect-the-dots. Does it look like what you expected?

Real-life data can be examined on a coordinate plane to look for relationships between the data. A **scatter plot** is one way to determine if two quantities are related. A scatter plot is a set of ordered pairs graphed on a coordinate plane where each ordered pair represents two data values. Once data can be seen visually on a scatter plot, it is possible to see whether or not there is a relationship between the two sets of data. Examples of data sets that might be examined on a scatter plot are height and weight, years of schooling and salary, or average temperature and latitude placement.

EXAMPLE 2

Derrick surveyed eight friends to determine if there is a relationship between height and shoe size.
a. Make a scatter plot of the data. Put height on the *x*-axis and shoe size on the *y*-axis.

Height (inches), *x*	60	72	65	63	74	69	64	59
Shoe Size, *y*	7	12	9	8	14	9	7	5

b. In general, how does shoe size change as height changes?

SOLUTIONS

a. Plot each pair of data values.

b. The scatter plot shows that as height increases, shoe size appears to increase.

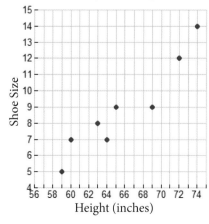

EXAMPLE 3

Draw a scatter plot to model the data given below. Describe the pattern seen in the scatter plot.

Year	Cost of First Class Stamp (in cents)
1985	22
1988	25
1991	29
1995	32
1999	33
2001	34
2002	37
2006	39
2007	41
2008	42

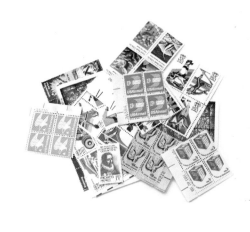

SOLUTION

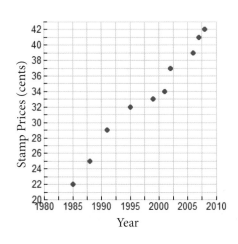

As time passes, stamp prices appear to rise steadily.

EXERCISES

1. Draw a coordinate plane with an *x*-axis and *y*-axis that go from −10 to 10. Label each axis, quadrant and the origin.

2. On the coordinate plane drawn in **Exercise 1**, graph and label the following ordered pairs.

A(4, 7)   B(−4, −1)   C(2, 0)   D(0, −9)   E(−1, 5)

3. Give the ordered pair for each point on the coordinate plane shown.

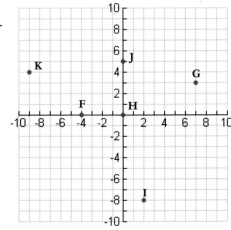

Tell whether each point described below is on the *x*-axis, *y*-axis or in Quadrant I, II, III or IV.

4. The *x*-coordinate is positive and the *y*-coordinate is negative.

5. The *x*-coordinate is 0 and the *y*-coordinate is positive.

6. Both coordinates are positive.

7. The *x*-coordinate is negative and the *y*-coordinate is 0.

8. Both coordinates are negative.

9. Mr. Harrison wanted to see if there was a relationship between the number of missing homework assignments his students had from the last chapter and how the students did on the chapter test. The data he collected is shown in the table below.

Number of Missing Assignments	2	0	4	6	1	3	4	0	1
Grade on Chapter Test	82%	96%	74%	50%	94%	80%	68%	100%	90%

    a. Draw a scatter plot to model the data. Put the number of missing assignments on the *x*-axis and the students' test scores on the *y*-axis.

    b. Describe the pattern seen in the scatter plot. Do you think this relationship is true for most students in your classes? Why or why not?

10. Brittany told her friend, "I think that as people get older, they don't watch as many movies." In order to verify her statement, she asked ten different people how many movies they had seen during the past month. Her survey results are shown on the scatter plot.

    a. Based on the data collected, would you agree or disagree with Brittany's statement? Defend your answer.

    b. Based on the scatter plot, could you predict how many movies a fifty-year-old watches? If so, how many? If not, why?

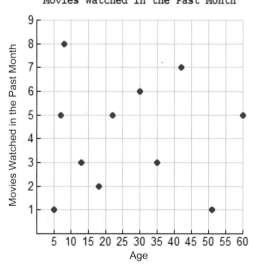

11. Jillian went for a run on the treadmill. Every so often she recorded her heart rate.

Minutes run	Heart Rate (beats per minute)
2	96
8	118
13	130
20	144
25	156
28	160
34	162
40	164

a. Draw a scatter plot to model the data she gathered.

b. Describe the pattern you see in the scatter plot.

c. What would you predict her heart rate would be after an hour of running? Why?

REVIEW

Solve each equation for _x_. Check the solution.

12. $5x - 7 = 23$

13. $17 = \frac{1}{2}(2x + 24)$

14. $-6(x - 1) = 66$

15. $4x + 3 = 3x + 14$

16. $7 = -2 + 2x$

17. $\frac{x}{3} - 1.6 = 5.8$

18. $-x + 9 = 2$

19. $3x + 1 = 11 - 2x$

TIC-TAC-TOE ~ SCATTER PLOT SURVEY

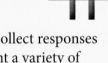

Scatter plots are used to show correlation between two items.

1. Choose one of the following pair of survey questions listed below. Collect responses from at least 15 individuals. Make sure you ask people who represent a variety of different groups (age, height, careers, etc). Record your data in a table.
   A. How tall are you (in inches)? What is your shoe size?
   B. What is your favorite number? How many years of school have you attended?
   C. How old are you? How many television shows do you watch each week?

2. Determine which item will be represented by the variable _x_ and which item will be represented by _y_. Explain how you made your decision.

3. Display your data in a scatter plot drawn on graph paper.

4. Based on your survey, do you believe the two items are correlated? Does this surprise you? Explain your answer.

TIC-TAC-TOE ~ INEQUALITIES

> > Greater Than
> < Less Than
> ≥ Greater Than or Equal To
> ≤ Less Than or Equal To

A mathematical sentence that contains >, <, ≥ or ≤ is an inequality. A solution to an inequality is any value that makes the inequality true.

For example: Given that $x \geq -1$, one solution to the inequality is 4 because $4 \geq -1$.

Solutions to an inequality can be graphed on a number line. When using the > or < inequality symbols, an open circle is used on the number line because the solution does not include the given number. For example, if $x > 2$, the solution cannot include 2 because 2 is not greater than 2. When using the ≥ or ≤ inequality symbols, a closed (or filled in) circle is used because the solution contains the given number.

Determining which direction the arrow should point is based on the relationship between the variable and the solution. For example, if $x \geq -1$ then the arrow will point to all numbers greater than -1.

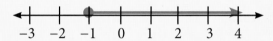

$$-3 \quad -2 \quad -1 \quad 0 \quad 1 \quad 2 \quad 3 \quad 4$$

Inequalities are solved using properties similar to those you used to solve equations. Use inverse operations to isolate the variable so the solution can be graphed on a number line.

One special rule applies to solving inequalities. Whenever you multiply or divide by a negative number on both sides of the equation, you must flip the inequality symbol. For example, < would become > if you multiply or divide by a negative when performing inverse operations.

For example: $-4x + 7 \leq 19$

$$-4x + 7 \leq 19$$
$$\underline{\quad -7 \quad\quad -7 \quad}$$
$$\frac{-4x}{-4} \leq \frac{12}{-4}$$
$$x \geq -3$$

> Reverse the inequality symbol when dividing by a negative.

Solve each inequality below. Graph the solution on a number line.

1. $2x + 7 > 15$

2. $\frac{x}{2} - 1 \geq -4$

3. $-3x - 4 < 5$

4. $5(x + 3) \leq 20$

5. $7 > \frac{x}{-4} + 6$

6. $9x < 2x - 35$

7. $-7 + 4x \geq 3 - 6x$

8. $2(x + 3) \geq 5x + 12$

9. $\frac{1}{2}x + 8 < x + 4$

REVIEW

BLOCK 1

Vocabulary

absolute value	Distributive Property	order of operations
algebraic expression	equation	ordered pair
axes (x-axis and y-axis)	equivalent expressions	quadrants
coefficient	inverse operations	scatter plot
constant	like terms	term
coordinate plane	origin	zero pair

Find the value of expressions using the order of operations.
Evaluate expressions.
Simplify expressions using the Distributive Property and combining like terms.
Use inverse operations to solve one-step equations.
Solve two-step equations.
Simplify and solve multi-step equations.
Graph points on the coordinate plane.

Lesson 1 ~ Order of Operations

• •

Evaluate each expression.

1. $6 + 7 \cdot 3 - 9$

2. $35 \div 7 \cdot 2 - 4^2$

3. $|4 - 8| + |8 - 1|$

4. $(-2 + 5)^2 - 10$

5. $2(11 - 5) - 10$

6. $\dfrac{9 + 11}{(1 + 1)^2}$

7. $\dfrac{-14 - 4}{2 + 1} - 5$

8. $\dfrac{7|11 - 4| + 1}{(-5)^2}$

9. $\frac{1}{2}(6 + 8) - 2(3 - 5)$

Lesson 2 ~ Evaluating Expressions

• •

Evaluate each expression for the given values of the variables.

10. $2x + 3$ when $x = 4$

11. $12 - 3f$ when $f = 1.2$

12. $\dfrac{2y - 1}{2y}$ when $y = 3$

13. $10(p + 5)$ when $p = -7$

14. $6a^2 - 14$ when $a = 3$

15. $7m + 1$ when $m = \frac{1}{2}$

Copy each table. Complete each table by evaluating the given expression for the values listed.

16.

x	$5x + 1$	Output
-2		
0		
$\frac{1}{2}$		
3		
7		

17.

x	$\dfrac{3x + 2}{4}$	Output
-3		
0		
4		
10		

Lesson 3 ~ The Distributive Property

Use the Distributive Property to simplify each expression.

18. $5(x + 4)$

19. $\frac{1}{4}(8x - 2)$

20. $-1(3x - 12)$

21. $6(3x - 10)$

22. $-3(-8x + 5)$

23. $0.1(15x + 5)$

Simplify each expression.

24. $3x + 7 + 4x - 2$

25. $3(x - 4) + 6$

26. $5(x - 1) - 5$

27. $3(x - 4) + 2(x + 1)$

28. $4x + 3x - 5x + 2 - x$

29. $6x + 40 + 4x - 15$

Write and simplify an expression for the perimeter of each figure.

30.

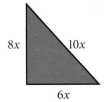

31.

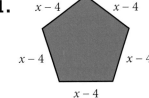

Lesson 4 ~ Solving One-Step Equations

Solve each equation. Check the solution.

32. $x + 13 = 35$

33. $\frac{x}{7} = -3$

34. $10x = 90$

35. $-8x = -44$

36. $\frac{1}{2}x = 10$

37. $3.7 = \frac{x}{6}$

Write an equation for each statement. Solve each equation. Check the solution.

38. The sum of seven and a number is 73.

39. Ten less than a number is 66.

40. Twenty-nine is equal to a number divided by three.

Solve each equation. Check the solution.

41. $10x - 8 = 92$

42. $-5x - 1 = 44$

43. $4 = \frac{x}{6} - 2$

44. $\frac{x}{7} + 1.3 = 2.1$

45. $2x - 7 = 4$

46. $\frac{1}{3}x + 3 = 3$

47. Kari is saving money for an MP3 player. She began the year with $30 of savings.
At the end of each month, Kari adds $14.
    a. How much will Kari have after 3 months have passed?
    b. Write a formula to calculate Kari's total savings (S) based on how many
        months (m) she has saved this year.
    c. The MP3 player Kari wants costs $170. Use your formula to determine how
        many months it will take for Kari to have enough to purchase the MP3 player.

Lesson 6 ~ Solving Multi-Step Equations

Solve each equation. Check the solution.

48. $6(x + 3) = 42$

49. $5x + 2 = 3x - 2$

50. $-4x + 9 = x - 11$

51. $2(x - 1) = 3x - 13$

52. $\frac{1}{4}(8x + 1) = 12\frac{1}{4}$

53. $9x + 4x - 7 = 3x - 17$

54. A bowling alley has two payment options for bowlers. Option A allows
bowlers to pay $3 per game. Option B allows bowlers to join the 'Elite
Bowling Club' for $15 plus an additional $1.50 per game.
    a. Write an expression for the cost of x games with Option A.
    b. Write an expression for the cost of x games with Option B.
    c. Set the two expressions equal to one another. Solve the equation. How
        many games would someone need to bowl to make both options cost the
        same amount?
    d. If Ray is going to bowl 14 games, which option should he choose? Why?

55. Julie had $400 in her savings account at the beginning of the summer. Each week she took $20 out of
her account. Stephen had $100 in his account at the beginning of summer. Each week he added $30
to his account.
    a. Write an expression for the amount in Julie's account after x weeks.
    b. Write an expression for the amount in Stephen's account after x weeks.
    c. Set the two expressions equal to each other. Solve the equation to determine how many weeks it took
        for Julie and Stephen to have the same amount in their accounts.

For problems 56 - 59 give the ordered pair for each point on the coordinate plane shown below.

56. A

57. B

58. C

59. D

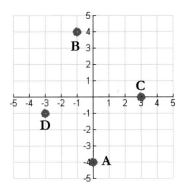

60. Give the coordinates of a point that could be found in Quadrant II.

61. Give the coordinates of a point that could be found on the *y*-axis.

62. Give the coordinates of a point that could be found in Quadrant IV.

63. Give the coordinates of the origin.

64. Jason noticed that there were lots of people at the park on a warm day. He decided to collect data comparing the outside temperature to the number of people at his neighborhood park on different days.

   a. Make a scatter plot of the data. Put temperature on the *x*-axis and the number of people at the park on the *y*-axis.

Temperature (F°)	60°	72°	86°	52°	74°	80°	66°	78°
Number of People at Park	6	8	14	3	9	10	4	7

   b. Is there a relationship between the weather outside and the number of people at the park? If so, what is the relationship?

   c. Based on the scatter plot, predict the number of people at the park when it is 100° outside. Do you think this is realistic? Why or why not?

CAREER FOCUS

RODGER
INSURANCE AGENCY OWNER
BAKER CITY, OREGON

I am the owner of an insurance agency that deals mostly with farmers. We consult with clients to help them understand how to protect themselves from disaster by having the right kind of insurance. We also offer prices for whatever coverage a client may need. If a customer decides to buy insurance, we deliver their policy and explain it to them. Our company tries to give excellent service so our clients will want to stay with us for a long time.

The amount of money a client must pay for insurance is determined by math formulas. Most of the time, calculations are done by computers. Some insurances, though, are still done without computers. One type of insurance where we do the math ourselves is crop insurance. If a farmer tells us he wants to get insurance on 500 tons of hay, we have to determine a couple of things. The first question to answer is how much they want the hay insured for. The next question is for how long they would like the hay covered. There is a table that gives all of the different rates of policies depending on those two questions. We can use the rates from the table to come up with a price for the farmer's policy.

Insurance agents also use math to determine fire insurance rates. An insurance agent has to add all the different costs that would go into rebuilding a house if it were to burn down. Some of these calculations can become pretty complicated. In many ways, it is just like a big story problem.

You do not need a college education to work in the insurance field, but it is a good idea to have one. There are many different career paths in insurance, and a college education will help you in whatever path you choose to follow.

Insurance is commissions-based. This means that you make a percentage of whatever amount of insurance you sell. The more you sell, the more money you make. The harder you work, the more you are rewarded.

I like being an insurance agency owner. As the owner I do a little bit of everything. I fix computers, answer phones, meet with clients and pay the employees and bills. No day is the same, and no day is ever a slow day. I also like the fact that the effort you put into the work affects how much you earn. Not all jobs are like that. Lastly, I like my career because it gives me a very satisfying feeling to know that I helped someone out when they encountered a situation in life that required insurance.

BLOCK 2 ~ LINEAR EQUATIONS

SEQUENCES AND SLOPE

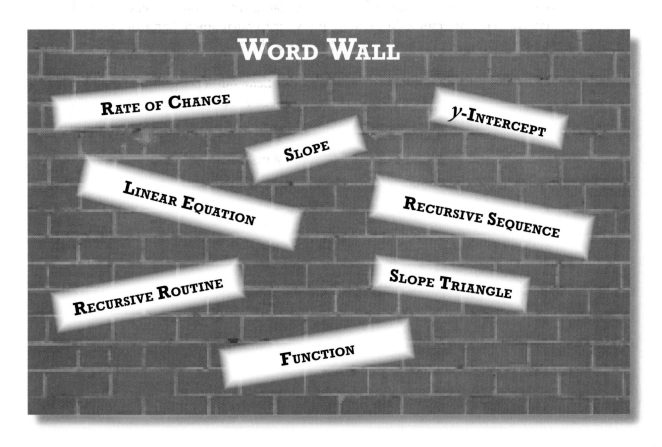

WORD WALL

RATE OF CHANGE

SLOPE

y-INTERCEPT

LINEAR EQUATION

RECURSIVE SEQUENCE

RECURSIVE ROUTINE

SLOPE TRIANGLE

FUNCTION

BLOCK 2 ~ SEQUENCES AND SLOPE
TIC - TAC - TOE

SLOPE METHODS

Create a flip book explaining how to find slope from tables, graphs and ordered pairs.

See page 83 for details.

CROSSING PATHS

Determine where two recursive sequences cross paths. Illustrate solutions with tables and graphs.

See page 49 for details.

CARD GAME

Make a card game where players create recursive routines and score points.

See page 54 for details.

GEOMETRIC SEQUENCES

Examine recursive sequences involving repeated multiplication. Write equations for these recursive routines.

See page 70 for details.

CHALLENGING TABLES

Find the rates of change and start values in challenging input-output tables.

See page 64 for details.

WRITING EQUATIONS FROM TABLES

Create a worksheet to help another student through the process of writing an equation for an input-output table.

See page 74 for details.

RATE APPLICATIONS

Find the rates of change in real-world situations. Write application problems.

See page 64 for details.

CHILDREN'S STORY

Write a children's story about recursive sequences. The main character encounters a recursive sequence and develops its equation.

See page 79 for details.

SIMILAR SLOPE TRIANGLES

Make discoveries about different size slope triangles formed on the same line.

See page 89 for details.

RECURSIVE ROUTINES

Write recursive routines and create recursive sequences.

A recursive sequence is an ordered list of numbers that begins with a start value. Each term in the sequence is generated by applying an operation to the term before it. This same operation is repeated to the resulting value. This process continues to make a sequence of terms.

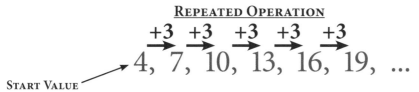

REPEATED OPERATION

$$\xrightarrow{+3} \xrightarrow{+3} \xrightarrow{+3} \xrightarrow{+3} \xrightarrow{+3}$$

START VALUE → 4, 7, 10, 13, 16, 19, ...

A recursive routine is described by stating the start value and the operation that is performed to get to the next term. In this case, the recursive routine for the sequence above is:

> Start Value: 4
>
> Operation: Add 3

EXAMPLE 1

For each of the following recursive sequences, state the start value, operation and the next three terms.

a. 8, 17, 26, 35, 44, ...

b. 6, 2, −2, −6, −10, ...

SOLUTIONS

a. Start Value = 8
   Operation = Add 9
   Next three terms: 53, 62, 71

b. Start Value = 6
   Operation = Subtract 4
   Next three terms: −14, −18, −22

EXPLORE!   **CALORIC RECURSIVE ROUTINES**

Step 1: Resting Metabolic Rate (RMR) represents the number of calories your body burns daily when at rest. In the table below, choose the weight and gender that best describes you to determine your approximate RMR. Record your value on your paper.

MALE

Weight (lbs)	RMR (kcal)
80	1290
90	1340
100	1400
120	1490
140	1600
160	1720
180	1830

FEMALE

Weight (lbs)	RMR (kcal)
80	1130
90	1170
100	1230
120	1320
140	1430
160	1550
180	1660

Step 2: Choose an activity that you would most like to participate in from the list below. Record your choice and the calories burned per minute.

Activity	Aerobics	Downhill Skiing	Bowling	Horseback Riding	Flag Football
Calories Burned per Minute	7	6	3	4	8

Step 3: Copy the table shown at right. Insert the name of your activity at the top of the first column.

Step 4: How many calories has your body burned during a full day before you participate in your chosen activity? What is this value called? Where would this fit in the table?

Step 5: Determine the total daily calories burned through the first five minutes of your activity. Continue your calculations to determine the total daily calories burned for 10 minutes, 20 minutes and 30 minutes.

Step 6: If you want to burn 2,000 total calories during one day. How many minutes will you need to participate in your activity? Is this reasonable?

Minutes Spent (*Insert activity*)	Total Daily Calories Burned
0	
1	
2	
3	
4	
5	
10	
20	
30	
	≈ 2,000

Step 7: Describe the recursive routine for your table (when going up one minute at a time) by giving the start value and the operation that must be performed to arrive at the next term.

RECURSIVE ROUTINE

Start Value: _____

Operation: _____

EXAMPLE 2

Find the missing values in each sequence. Identify the start value and the operation that must be performed to arrive at the next term.
a. 25, 19, 13, _____, 1, _____, _____
b. 32, 45, _____, _____, 84, _____

SOLUTIONS

a. The numbers in the list are going DOWN 6 each time.
Start Value: 25
Operation: Subtract 6
Completed List: 25, 19, 13, <u>7</u>, 1, <u>–5</u>, <u>–11</u>

b. The numbers in the list are increasing by 13 each time.
Start Value: 32
Operation: Add 13
Completed List: 32, 45, <u>58</u>, <u>71</u>, 84, <u>97</u>

USING YOUR CALCULATOR… TO CREATE A RECURSIVE ROUTINE

Most scientific and graphing calculators can perform a repeated calculation to create a sequence of numbers.
- Enter the start value.
- Press ENTER or =.
- Enter the operation.
- Press ENTER or = repeatedly to generate the recursive sequence.

EXAMPLE 3

For each sequence, describe the recursive routine by giving the starting value and operation. Give the 15th term.

a. 35, 50, 65, 80, …
b. 10, 1, −8, −17, …

SOLUTIONS

a.
$$\overset{+15}{35,}\ \overset{+15}{50,}\ \overset{+15}{65,}\ \overset{+15}{80,}\ …$$
START VALUE

Start Value: 35
Operation: Add 15 (or +15)
15th Term: 245

> Try using a calculator to find the 15th term.

b.
$$\overset{-9}{10,}\ \overset{-9}{1,}\ \overset{-9}{-8,}\ \overset{-9}{-17,}\ …$$
START VALUE

Start Value: 10
Operation: Subtract 9 (or − 9)
15th Term: −116

EXERCISES

Copy each sequence of numbers and fill in the missing values. Identify the start value and the operation that must be performed to arrive at the next term.

1. 3, 5, ____, 9, ____, ____

2. 125, ____, 175, 200, ____, ____

3. 27, 22, 17, ____, ____, ____

4. ____, ____, −5, −9, −13, ____

5. 23, ____, 45, 56, ____, ____

6. $4\frac{1}{2}$, 5, ____, ____, $6\frac{1}{2}$, ____

7. ____, 2.7, 3.1, ____, 3.9, ____

8. −42, −22, ____, ____, ____, 58

9. Deidre weighs 100 pounds. She enjoys downhill skiing at Mt. Hood Meadows.
    a. Copy the table to the right. Use the table in the EXPLORE! to determine Deidre's
    means subtraction. resting metabolic rate (RMR). Insert it in the table for 0
    minutes skiing.
    b. How many calories will Deidre burn each
    minute she skis?

c. Fill in the total calories she will burn in a full day for each
    added minute she skis.

d. Deidre ends up skiing for 40 minutes. How many TOTAL
    calories did she burn on that day if she participated in no
    other activities?

Minutes Spent Downhill Skiing	Total Daily Calories Burned
0	
1	
2	
3	
4	

10. Squares, each 1 centimeter by 1 centimeter, are placed next to each other (one at a time) to form a long
strip of squares.

    a. What is the perimeter of the first figure using just one square?
    b. What is the perimeter of the figure using two squares? Three squares?
    c. Draw the next two figures in the pattern. What are the perimeters of these figures?
    d. Write the recursive routine (start value and operation) that describes the perimeters.
    e. Predict the perimeter of the figure that has 14 of these squares in one long strip.

 **For each sequence describe the recursive routine (start value and operation). Give the 9th term in the
sequence.**

11. 8, 16, 24, 32 …

12. 10.5, 9.4, 8.3, 7.2 …

13. 9, 5, 1, −3 …

14. $\frac{1}{3}$, 1, $1\frac{2}{3}$, $2\frac{1}{3}$ …

15. Each block is 1 centimeter by 1 centimeter.
    a. Draw the next two figures in the following pattern.
    b. What is the perimeter of the first figure using just one square?
    c. What is the perimeter of the second figure? The third figure?
    d. Write the recursive routine (start value and operation) that describes the perimeters.
    e. Predict the perimeter of the seventh figure in this pattern.

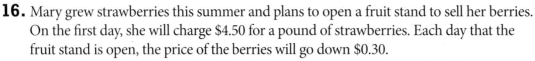

16. Mary grew strawberries this summer and plans to open a fruit stand to sell her berries.
On the first day, she will charge $4.50 for a pound of strawberries. Each day that the
fruit stand is open, the price of the berries will go down $0.30.
    a. Write a recursive routine that describes the cost of the strawberries.
    b. Write the sequence of numbers that shows the price of strawberries
    each day for the first five days the fruit stand is open.
    c. On what day will the price of the strawberries drop below $2.00?
    d. When will she be giving away the strawberries for free?

 17. Generate your own recursive sequence. Describe the recursive routine by giving the start value
and operation. List the first five numbers in the sequence. What is the 20th term in your sequence?

Copy each table. Complete each table by evaluating the given expression for the values listed.

18.

x	$6x + 7$	Output
−2		
0		
$\frac{1}{2}$		
5		
10		

19.

x	$3(x - 1)$	Output
−3		
0		
2.2		
8		
21		

20. Draw a coordinate plane that goes from −10 to 10 on the x-axis and −10 to 10 on the y-axis. Graph and label the following points: A(1, 4), B(3, −5), C(0, 2), D(−2, −1), E(−5, 0).

TIC-TAC-TOE ~ CROSSING PATHS

Recursive routines that represent linear relationships often cross paths or intersect at one point. To find where the sequences intersect, you can create an input-output table or make a graph. Each set of recursive routines below will intersect at one point. Find the point of intersection.

Use an input-output table to determine where the two recursive routines intersect.

1. **Routine A**
 Start Value = 7
 Operation = +2

  Routine B
 Start Value = 19
 Operation = −4

2. **Routine A**
 Start Value = −9
 Operation = +7

  Routine B
 Start Value = 19
 Operation = +3

3. **Routine A**
 Start Value = 120
 Operation = −12

  Routine B
 Start Value = −80
 Operation = +28

See Lesson 9 for information on input-output tables and graphing.

Use a graph to determine where the two recursive routines intersect.

4. **Routine A**
 Start Value = 4
 Operation = +3

  Routine B
 Start Value = 20
 Operation = −1

5. **Routine A**
 Start Value = −2
 Operation = +5

  Routine B
 Start Value = 13
 Operation = +2

6. Which method did you prefer for finding the point of intersection? Why?

LINEAR PLOTS

LESSON 9

Create linear plots for recursive sequences.

Aroldo attended the State Fair with his friends in August. The entry fee was $8 and each ride he went on cost an additional $2. The graph below shows the total Aroldo may have spent depending on the number of rides he went on.

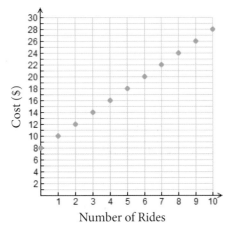

This situation can also be shown using a table. Take each ordered pair on the graph and put it in the corresponding spot in the table.

Number of Rides	0	1	2	3	4	5	6	7	8	9	10
Cost ($)	8	10	12	14	16	18	20	22	24	26	28

The cost (y-coordinate) based on the number of rides can be described by a recursive routine:

Start Value: $8
Operation: Add $2

Notice that the points on the graph form a straight line. The graph shows that there is a linear relationship between the number of rides he went on and his total cost. Aroldo's total cost at the fair is directly related to the number of rides he went on. When real-life situations are examined mathematically you will find that many can be described as having a linear relationship. Can you think of any other situations that might have a starting value and then go up or down in equal steps?

In a linear relationship, the *y*-coordinates follow a recursive routine when the *x*-coordinates in a table or scatter plot increase in equal increments. When a graph or table shows the *x*-coordinate increasing by 1, the recursive sequence of the *y*-coordinates describes the linear relationship.

EXAMPLE 1

Describe the linear relationship given by the *y*-coordinates on each graph by stating the recursive routine and the first 10 numbers in the recursive sequence.

a.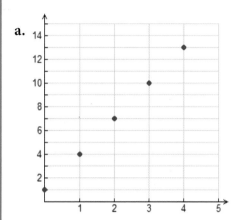

b.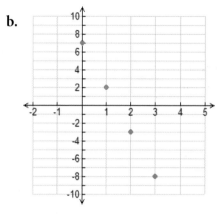

SOLUTIONS

a. The *y*-coordinates that are shown are 1, 4, 7, 10, 13 …
The recursive routine can be described by the following rules:
  Start Value: 1
  Operation: Add 3
  Using this recursive routine you can determine that the first 10 *y*-coordinates in this sequence are: 1, 4, 7, 10, 13, 16, 19, 22, 25, 28.

b. The *y*-coordinates that are shown are 7, 2, −3, −8 …
The recursive routine can be described by the following rules:
  Start Value: 7
  Operation: Subtract 5
  Using this recursive routine you can determine that the first 10 *y*-coordinates in the sequence are: 7, 2, −3, −8, −13, −18, −23, −28, −33, −38.

Sometimes it is useful to generate a table to represent the ordered pairs of recursive sequences shown on a linear plot. This can be done by creating an input-output table for the *x*- and *y*-coordinates. For example, the ordered pairs of **Part A** in **Example 1** can be converted to a table by recording each *x*-coordinate with its corresponding *y*-coordinate.

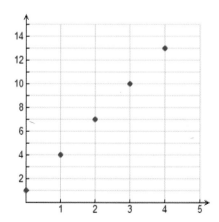

Input x	Output y
0	1
1	4
2	7
3	10
4	13
5	16

Input-output tables can be written horizontally or vertically.

Input x	0	1	2	3	4	5
Output y	1	4	7	10	13	16

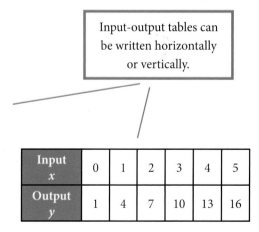

EXAMPLE 2

Jerome throws the shot put for Newbridge High School. Coming into the season, his personal best was 42 feet. Each week, his shot put throws increase by 0.5 feet. Create a linear plot that represents this situation. Write a recursive routine to describe it.

SOLUTION

Start Value: 42 Feet
Operation: Add 0.5 Feet

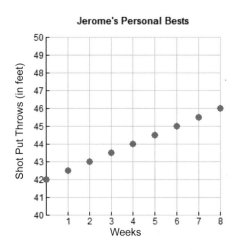

Jerome's Personal Bests

RECURSIVE ROUTINES FOR LINEAR RELATIONSHIPS

Start Value: corresponds to an *x*-value of 0.
Operation: the amount the *y*-value increases or decreases for each unit on the *x*-axis.

EXERCISES

Describe the linear relationship given by the *y*-coordinates on each linear plot by stating the start value and operation. Create an input-output table showing the ordered pairs on each linear plot.

1.

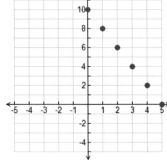

2.

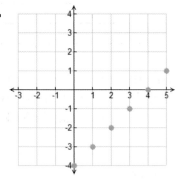

3.

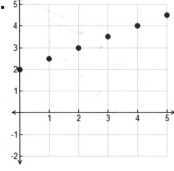

4.

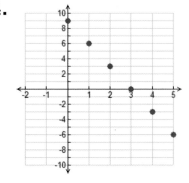

52 *Lesson 9 ~ Linear Plots*

5.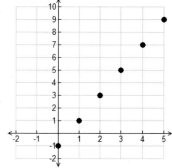

6.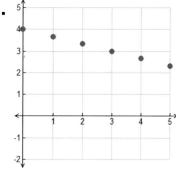

7.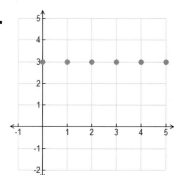

8.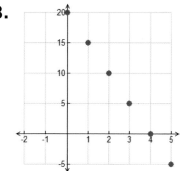

9. Kirk chose to go down the steepest, fastest water slide in the aquatic park. The linear plot shows how high off the ground Kirk is, based on the number of seconds he has been on the slide.

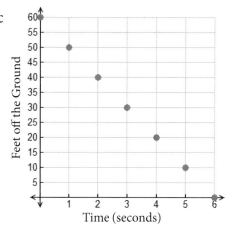

    a. Copy the input-output table shown and fill in all the ordered pairs shown on the linear plot.

Time (seconds), x	Feet off the Ground, y
0	
1	
2	

    b. Write the recursive routine for Kirk's ride down the slide.
    c. What does the start value represent in real life?
    d. How long does it take for Kirk to get to the bottom of the slide?

Create a linear plot for the first five ordered pairs for the given recursive routine. Remember that the start value corresponds to an *x*-value of 0.

10.
Start Value: 8
Operation: Subtract 3

11.
Start Value: 1
Operation: Add $\frac{1}{2}$

12. Create a recursive routine by picking a start value and operation (adding or subtracting).
    a. Record your recursive routine on your homework.
    b. Create a linear plot for at least five points in your recursive sequence.
    c. Create an input-output table that shows the *x*- and *y*-coordinates for the linear plot you generated.

Write and simplify an expression for the area of each figure.

Area of Rectangle = bh Area of Triangle = $\frac{1}{2}bh$

13.
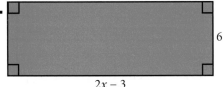
6

2x − 3

14.
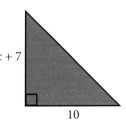
x + 7

10

15.
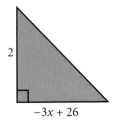
2

−3x + 26

16.
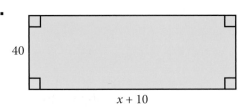
40

x + 10

TIC-TAC-TOE ~ CARD GAME

Use a regular deck of playing cards for this activity. Take out all the face cards (Jacks, Queens and Kings). Create a card game that can be played with two people. The card game must make the players use recursive routines to earn "points". Be creative with your rules.

Some ideas to think about:

◆ How many cards does each person start with?
◆ Do some colors and/or suits represent negative integers or subtraction?
◆ How will the cards be used to determine a start value of a recursive routine?
◆ How will the cards be used to determine an operation of a recursive routine?
◆ How are points scored or how does the person progress towards a finish line?
◆ Do players ever have to find a specific term in the sequence based on a number they draw from the deck?

Once you have designed your game, ask two different pairs of people to try it out. Ask each player to write a short review of your game once they have played it. Read the reviews and write a one-page paper summarizing the feedback. Also include in your paper any changes you would make in the rules before the game was played again. Turn in your paper along with the original set of rules for your game.

Represent recursive routine applications with graphs, tables and words.

Recursive routines are useful when dealing with a variety of real-world situations. Recursive routines can be illustrated with graphs, tables and by words. Using multiple ways of showing a recursive routine helps to reach a variety of audiences. It is important to think about what type of graphic (table, graph, words, etc.) best illustrates each situation.

EXPLORE!   **SAVING AND SPENDING**

William and his sister, Jennifer, each worked summer jobs. William mowed lawns in his neighborhood. Jennifer baby-sat for two different families. By the end of the summer, William had put $410 in a savings account. Jennifer put $275 in her own account. After school started, Jennifer continued baby-sitting and earned $20 per week. She put all of her earnings in her savings account. William stopped working and withdrew $15 per week from his savings account for spending money.

Step 1: Write a recursive routine (start value and operation) for the amount in William's savings account each week after school begins.

Step 2: Write a recursive routine for the amount in Jennifer's savings account each week after school begins.

Step 3: Copy the input-output tables shown below and fill in each for the first 10 weeks after school starts.

Weeks After School Starts	William's Total Savings
0	
1	
2	

Weeks After School Starts	Jennifer's Total Savings
0	
1	
2	

Step 4: On the SAME first-quadrant coordinate plane, graph William and Jennifer's total savings for the first ten weeks. Use ◆ to designate Jennifer's amounts and ▪ to represent William's amounts. Put weeks on the *x*-axis and $$ on the *y*-axis.

Step 5: After what week does Jennifer have more money than her brother? Which illustration (table, graph or recursive routine) best shows this?

EXAMPLE 1

Matt pays a fee of $25 per month for his cell phone plan. He is charged $0.15 per text message he sends or receives.

a. Write a recursive routine that describes Matt's monthly cell phone bill based on the number of text messages he sent or received.

b. Create an input-output table for the first ten text messages.

c. Create a linear plot that shows his total monthly bill for up to ten text messages.

d. Determine Matt's total bill for the month of January if he sent or received 42 text messages.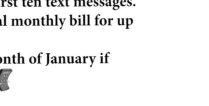

SOLUTIONS

a. Start Value = $25
   Operation = Add $0.15 (or + 0.15)

b.

Text Messages Sent or Received	Total Bill
0	$25
1	$25.15
2	$25.30
3	$25.45
4	$25.60
5	$25.75
6	$25.90
7	$26.05
8	$26.20
9	$26.35
10	$26.50

c.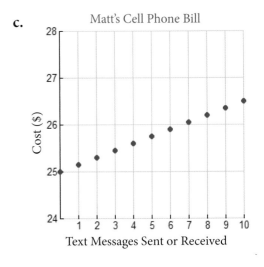

d. Use a calculator. Enter the start value, 25, and press ENTER or =. Then enter your operation, + 0.15, and press ENTER or = 42 times. You should arrive at the answer of $31.30.

A few things to remember when creating tables and graphing:

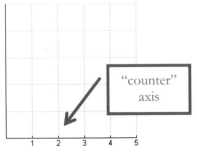

"counter" axis

♦ Always put the "counter" in the first column of a table and on the *x*-axis of a graph. The "counter" is the item the *y*-value is dependent on. It will start at zero and go up by one each time.

♦ Most real-world situations take place in the first quadrant. Think about your situation before graphing and decide if negative numbers would ever make sense. For example, you will not have a negative amount for the cost of a cell phone bill, so you will only need to use the first quadrant.

♦ Choose a range (lowest to the highest number) for the *y*-axis that allows the viewer of your graph to see all points easily. Also, make sure your increments on the *y*-axis are reasonable.

EXERCISES

Determine an appropriate range for the *y*-axis. State what increments you would use on the graph.

1.

Minutes	Distance Traveled
0	8
1	20
2	32
3	44
4	56
5	68

2.

Sales Made	Salary
0	$120
1	$150
2	$180
3	$210
4	$240
5	$270

3.

Years	Car's Worth
0	$12,000
1	$10,500
2	$9,000
3	$7,500
4	$6,000
5	$4,500

4. Jackson got his driving license one year ago. When Jackson got his driver's license, his car insurance cost $82 per month. Each time he gets a speeding ticket, his insurance goes up $26 per month.

    a. Write a recursive routine that describes Jackson's monthly car insurance bill based on the number of tickets he has received.

    b. Create an input-output table for 0 to 5 speeding tickets.

    c. Create a linear plot that shows his total monthly bill through the first five tickets.

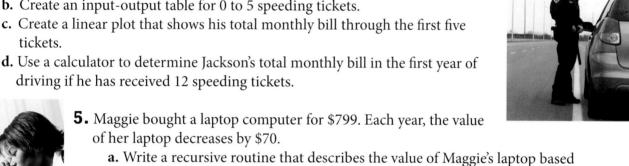

    d. Use a calculator to determine Jackson's total monthly bill in the first year of driving if he has received 12 speeding tickets.

5. Maggie bought a laptop computer for $799. Each year, the value of her laptop decreases by $70.

    a. Write a recursive routine that describes the value of Maggie's laptop based on the number of years she has owned it.

    b. Create an input-output table for the value of the laptop for 0 to 5 years.

    c. Create a linear plot that shows the value of the laptop through the first five years.

    d. Use a calculator to determine how many years it will take before the laptop is not worth anything.

6. Fran borrowed $200 from his parents to buy a mountain bike. Each week, he uses $14 of his allowance to pay back his parents.

    a. Write a recursive routine that describes the total amount Fran owes his parents based on the number of weeks that have passed since he borrowed the money.

    b. Create an input-output table that shows the amount he still owes for 0 to 5 weeks.

    c. Create a linear plot that shows the amount Fran still owes his parents through the first five weeks.

    d. Use a calculator to determine how many weeks it will take before Fran has paid back his parents. How much was his last payment?

7. Quincy hiked up a slope in Desert Shores, California (one of the few places below sea level in the United States). He began at an elevation 61 feet below sea level. Each minute that he hiked, he rose 7 feet in elevation.

   a. Write a recursive routine that describes Quincy's elevation based on the number of minutes he hiked.

   b. Create an input-output table to find his elevation for 0 to 10 minutes of hiking.

   c. Create a linear plot that shows Quincy's change in elevation through the first 10 minutes.

   d. How many minutes did it take for Quincy to get above sea level?

8. Victor and Mike had a pizza-eating contest. Victor had already eaten three pieces when the competition started. Mike had only eaten one piece. Once the competition started, Victor was able to eat $\frac{1}{2}$ of a piece every minute. Mike was able to eat a little faster. He ate $\frac{3}{4}$ of a piece every minute.

   a. Write two recursive routines, one that describes Victor's pizza-eating and the other describing Mike's pizza-eating. Label them accordingly.

   b. The pizza-eating competition lasted for 8 minutes. Create two input-output tables that show the number of pieces each boy had eaten for each of the first 8 minutes.

   c. Who won the competition at the end of 8 minutes?

9. When Kathy was born, her grandparents started an account for her college education with $1,000 in it. Each year, on her birthday, they add $250.

   a. Write a recursive routine that gives the amount of money in Kathy's account based on her age, not including interest.

   b. Determine the total amount her grandparents will have contributed after her 18th birthday.

   c. Overall, the entire account earned 28% interest. Determine the total amount the account was worth when she withdrew it after her eighteenth birthday.

REVIEW

Find the missing values in each sequence. Identify the start value and the operation that must be performed to arrive at the next term.

10. $-14, -11,$ _____, _____, $-2,$ _____

11. $5.8, 4.6,$ _____, $2.2,$ _____, _____

12. $9,$ _____, $21,$ _____, $33,$ _____

13. $\frac{1}{3}, 1,$ ___, $2\frac{1}{3},$ ___, ___

Solve each equation. Check the solution.

14. $x + 28 = 102$

15. $\frac{x}{6} = -7$

16. $-3x + 5 = 38$

17. $5x + 7 = 7x - 9$

18. $3 = \frac{x}{2} - 1.5$

19. $2x + 7 = 4$

RATE OF CHANGE

LESSON 11

Calculate rates of change and start values.

So far in **Block 2**, you have been looking at many different recursive routines. Each recursive sequence you have examined represents a linear relationship. This means that when you plot the points of the sequence on a coordinate plane, the points fall into a straight line. For each recursive routine, you have been able to define the operation that allows you to move from one number in the sequence to the next because you have been told how much to increase or decrease for each step.

There are many situations where the operation is not given for just one step. For example:

> Colton eats 560 calories in 10 minutes.
> Luke paints 72 pictures in 3 days.
> Karen goes down 90 steps in 4 minutes.

In order to determine the operation needed for each situation, you must calculate the **rate of change**. The rate of change can be found by calculating the change in the output (or y-values) divided by the change in input (x-values). It is also called the unit rate. It is important to think about which term is being used as the 'counter' and place that term in the denominator of the rate because it is your x-value. Time is the most common 'counter'.

You must also determine if a situation is giving you increasing numbers in the recursive sequence (pictures painted per day, calories eaten per minute) or decreasing numbers in the sequence (steps descended per minute). This will help in deciding if you are adding or subtracting your "rate of change" amount.

Situation	Rate	Rate of Change	Operation
Colton eats 560 calories in 10 minutes.	$\dfrac{560 \text{ calories}}{10 \text{ minutes}}$	$\dfrac{56 \text{ calories}}{1 \text{ minute}}$	Add 56
Luke paints 72 pictures in 3 days.	$\dfrac{72 \text{ pictures}}{3 \text{ days}}$	$\dfrac{24 \text{ pictures}}{1 \text{ day}}$	Add 24
Karen goes down 90 steps in 4 minutes.	$\dfrac{90 \text{ steps}}{4 \text{ minutes}}$	$\dfrac{-22.5 \text{ steps}}{1 \text{ minute}}$	Subtract 22.5

INCREASING?   DECREASING?

EXAMPLE 1

Determine the rate of change for each situation. State the operation that would occur in the recursive routine.
a. Jessica loses $580 in 20 days in the stock market.
b. Patrick earned $53 for delivering 10 packages.

SOLUTIONS

a. The 'counter' is the number of days so this term goes in the denominator.

$$\frac{-\$580}{20 \text{ days}} = \frac{-\$29}{1 \text{ day}}$$

(÷20, ÷20)

She is losing money, so the operation involves subtraction.
Operation = Subtract $29

b. The 'counter' is the number of packages.

$$\frac{\$53}{10 \text{ packages}} = \frac{\$5.30}{1 \text{ package}}$$

(÷10, ÷10)

He is earning money, so the operation involves addition.
Operation = Add $5.30

In some situations, information will be given to you in an input-output table. In those cases, you must be able to determine the rate of change by locating numbers on the table that will lead you to the rate of change.

RATE OF CHANGE

The rate of change is the change in *y*-values over the change in *x*-values: $\frac{\text{change in } y\text{-values}}{\text{change in } x\text{-values}}$

Once the rate of change is determined, locate or calculate the start value from the table.
The start value is the *y*-value that is paired with the *x*-coordinate of zero.

EXAMPLE 2

Determine the rate of change and start value for the input-output table.

x	y
−1	1
0	4
1	7
2	10
3	13

SOLUTION

Choose two ordered pairs. Look for two consecutive numbers in the 'counter' column.

Change in *x*-values = +1

x	y
−1	1
0	4
1	7
2	10
3	13

Change in *y*-values = +3

Calculate the rate of change.

$$\frac{\text{change in } y\text{-values}}{\text{change in } x\text{-values}} = \frac{+3}{+1} = +3$$

The start value is 4 because it is the *y*-value that is paired with an *x*-value of 0.

In some tables the *x*-coordinate of 0 is not listed. This means that the start value is not given. In order to find the start value you must first find the rate of change. Use the rate of change to work forward or backward to find the *y*-value that is paired with 0.

EXAMPLE 3

The rate of change in the table is −2. Find the start value.

x	y
2	6
3	4
4	2
5	0

SOLUTION

Rewrite the table to include *x*-coordinates to 0.

x	y
0	
1	
2	6
3	4

The rate of change is −2. Work backwards to get to the *x*-coordinate of 0 by doing the opposite of the rate of change. Add 2 for each step.

x	y	
0	10	+2
1	8	+2
2	6	
3	4	

The start value is 10.

EXAMPLE 4

Find the start value and rate of change for the input-output table.

x	y
−2	−9
3	11
7	27
9	35
12	47

SOLUTION

Find the rate of change by selecting two pairs of numbers.
Find the change in *x* and the change in *y*.

Change in *x*-values = +2

x	y
−2	−9
3	11
7	27
9	35
12	47

Change in *y*-values = +8

Calculate the rate of change.

$$\frac{\text{change in } y\text{-values}}{\text{change in } x\text{-values}} = \frac{+8}{+2} = +4$$

EXAMPLE 4
SOLUTION
(CONTINUED)

Use the rate of change to work forwards from $x = -2$ to find the y-value paired with the x-coordinate of 0.

x	y	
-2	-9	+4
-1	-5	+4
0	-1	

The start value is -1.
The rate of change is $+4$.

EXERCISES

Determine the rate of change for each situation.

1. George collected 18 bugs in 9 days.

2. Over 6 days Theo spent $336.

3. Michiko took 760 steps during a 15 minute run.

4. Natalie spent $4.80 for 8 roses.

Determine the rate of change and start value for each table.

5.

x	y
0	5
1	9
2	13
3	17
4	21

6.

x	y
-2	12
-1	9
0	6
1	3
2	0

7.

x	y
0	-3
3	0
5	2
6	3
8	5

8.

x	y
-2	-4
1	2
3	6
5	10
8	16

9.

x	y
-1	1
2	-5
4	-9
6	-13
9	-19

10.

x	y
-4	2
-2	3
-1	3.5
2	5
6	7

Use the given rate of change and start value to complete each table.

11.

x	y
0	
1	
2	
3	
4	
5	

Rate of Change = +8
Start Value = 1

12.

x	y
-1	
	4.8
1	
2	
3	12.6
4	

Rate of Change = +2.6
Start Value = 4.8

13.

x	y
	18
-1	
0	
	3
3	
6	

Rate of Change = -5
Start Value = 8

14. Jim-Bob's Car Rental Company charges a set fee for renting a car and an additional amount per mile driven. Frank has rented from Jim-Bob's three times and his charges are shown in the table to the right.

    a. How much does Jim-Bob charge per mile driven?

    b. What is the set fee for renting a car at Jim-Bob's?

    c. How much would a car rental cost if Frank drove 30 miles?

Miles Driven	Cost
4	$17.60
10	$20.00
22	$24.80

15. Mark moved into a new house and believes his bedroom will soon be taken over by ants. In the table shown below, Mark records the number of ants in his bedroom on different days since he moved in.

Days Since Mark Moved In	Number of Ants
3	66
5	90
9	138
13	186
15	210

    a. How many ants are moving into Mark's bedroom each day?

    b. How many ants were in his room when he first moved in?

    c. If this pattern continues, how many ants will be in his room after 3 weeks?

16. Mario rides his scooter to work each day. He is able to travel 0.5 miles per minute. He lives 4.7 miles from work.

    a. Copy the table and fill in the distance Mario has left to work based on each minute he has traveled from his home. Continue the table until he has arrived at work.

    b. What is the rate of change in this situation?

    c. Can you figure out exactly (to the second) how long Mario's trip is? If so, how long is it?

Minutes Traveled	Distance to Work
0	4.7
1	
2	
3	

REVIEW

Each input-output table represents a real-world situation. Determine an appropriate range for the *y*-axis. State what increments you would use on the *y*-axis.

17.

Hours	Distance Traveled
0	45
1	75
2	105
3	135
4	165
5	195

18.

Days	Plant Height
0	0
1	0.2
2	0.4
3	0.6
4	0.8
5	1.0

19.

Lawns Mowed	Profit
0	−$50
1	−$30
2	−$10
3	$10
4	$30
5	$50

TIC-TAC-TOE ~ CHALLENGING TABLES

Find the equation that represents the linear relationship in each table. Show all work.

1.

x	y
−3	1.5
0	2.7
2	3.5
6	5.1
8	5.9

2.

x	y
−8	1500
−3	875
4	0
9	−625
14	−1250

3.

x	y
−15	0
−12	1
−10	$1\frac{2}{3}$
−6	3
−1	$4\frac{2}{3}$

4.

x	y
−8	84
2	44
7	24
10	12
15	−8

5.

x	y
1	0.3
3	0.06
5	−0.18
7	−0.42
11	−0.9

6.

x	y
−2	2
3	$4\frac{1}{2}$
7	$6\frac{1}{2}$
10	8
12	9

TIC-TAC-TOE ~ RATE APPLICATIONS

Rates of change are calculated in many situations. Determine the rate of change in each situation given below. Assume each situation forms a linear relationship.

1. Ryan and Silas each bought a package of paper. Ryan bought 7 pencils with his paper for $1.96. Silas bought 12 of the same pencils with his paper for $3.36. Find the cost per pencil.

2. Kendra was at an elevation of −45 feet after 5 minutes of hiking. She was at −3 feet after eleven minutes. What was her rate of change in elevation in feet per minute?

3. Owen was 5.2 miles from home 10 minutes after school was over. He arrived home 30 minutes after school was over. What was his rate of speed going home from school?

Create a worksheet of 10 of your own rate problems. Type or neatly print the problems. Include the answers on a separate sheet of paper.

RECURSIVE ROUTINES TO EQUATIONS

LESSON 12

Write linear equations from recursive routines.

In this lesson you will learn how to take a recursive routine and determine the linear equation that represents the situation. When the solutions of a linear equation are graphed, they form a line. Almost all linear equations are also linear functions. A function is a pairing of input and output values according to a specific rule.

One common form of a linear equation is $y = b + mx$ where b represents the start value and m represents the rate of change.

EXPLORE!

MODELING WITH EQUATIONS

Vendors at the local Farmer's Market sell a variety of produce and homemade products. Examine each vendor's situation and write a linear equation that models their profits.

Step 1: Peter sells corn at his booth in the Farmer's Market. His start-up cost for his business was $200 which he spent on seeds, fertilizer and water. What number would represent the start value for his situation: 200 or −200? Why?

Step 2: Peter earns $0.25 for each ear of corn he sells. What number represents his rate of change: 0.25 or −0.25? Why?

Step 3: One form of a linear equation is $y = b + mx$. The b represents the start value and m represents the rate of change. Write a linear equation to represent Peter's total profits.

Step 4: Nakisha sells homemade candles at the Farmer's Market. She recorded her total profit for the first five candles sold in the table at the right. What is the start value for her business? What is the rate of change?

Step 5: Write a linear equation in the form of $y = b + mx$ to represent Nakisha's total profits at the Farmer's Market.

Step 6: Nakisha sold a total of 24 candles. Use your linear equation to determine her total profits.

Candles Sold, x	Total Profits, y
0	−$10
1	−$7
2	−$4
3	−$1
4	$2
5	$5

Step 7: Luke opened a booth at the Farmer's Market. He had a positive balance of $300 in his bank account. He paid $50 each week to rent his booth. He had trouble selling his products. His total savings is shown in the graph at the right. What is the recursive routine for this graph? Write a linear equation to represent this situation.

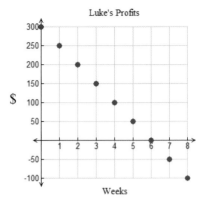

Step 8: One student summarized writing linear equations with the graphic below. How would you know whether to put a + or − between the start value and the rate of change in different situations?

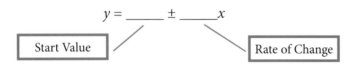

$$y = \underline{\hspace{1cm}} \pm \underline{\hspace{1cm}} x$$

Start Value   Rate of Change

Step 9: Write a linear equation in the form $y = b + mx$ for each recursive routine:

    a. Start Value = 4   Rate of Change = +5
    b. Start Value = −7   Rate of Change = +2
    c. Start Value = 0   Rate of Change = −12
    d. Start Value = −8   Rate of Change = +0

WRITING LINEAR EQUATIONS FROM RECURSIVE ROUTINES

1. Determine the rate of change.
2. Determine the start value from a described situation, graph or table.
3. Write the linear equation by filling in the start value (*b*) and rate of change (*m*) in the equation:

$$y = b + mx$$

You have found the start value in a recursive routine by looking at tables. It is the number paired with an *x*-value of 0. The start value can also be located on a graph as the point on the *y*-axis.

x	y
−1	−5
0	−2
1	1
2	4
3	7

Start Value

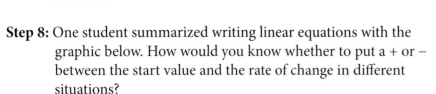

Linear equations represent the start value using the variable *b*. The start value (*b*) is also called the *y-intercept*. The *y*-intercept is the value of *y* where the graph crosses the *y*-axis or the number paired with an *x*-value of 0 in a table.

EXAMPLE 1

Write the linear equation for each recursive routine.

a. Rate of Change = +4
  Start Value = −23

b. Rate of Change = −0.3
  y-intercept = 2.8

c. Rate of Change = +2
  y-intercept = 0

d. Rate of Change = 0
  Start Value = 7

SOLUTIONS

a. Insert the rate of change and the start value into the equation $y = b + mx$. Remember, the rate of change is always the coefficient of the *x*-variable because the *x*-variable counts how many "steps" to take.
$$y = -23 + 4x$$

b. Insert the rate of change and the *y*-intercept into the equation. Remember, the *y*-intercept is just another way to refer to the start value.
$$y = 2.8 - 0.3x$$

c. Insert the rate of change and the *y*-intercept into the equation.
$$y = 0 + 2x \rightarrow y = 2x$$

> Adding 0 does not affect the value of the equation. It does not need to be written.

d. A rate of change equal to 0 cancels out the *x*-term.
$$y = 7 + 0x \rightarrow y = 7$$

EXAMPLE 2

Determine the rate of change and *y*-intercept (start value) for each table. Write a linear equation that represents each table.

a.

x	y
0	6
1	4
2	2
3	0
4	−2
5	−4

b.

x	y
−1	−2
1	8
4	23
6	33
9	48
12	63

SOLUTIONS

a. The start value is the *y*-value that matches with the *x*-value of 0. The start value is 6.

The rate of change is calculated by determining the change in the *y*-values divided by the change in the *x*-values.

x	y
0	6
1	4
2	2
3	0
4	−2
5	−4

Change in *x*-values = +1   Change in *y*-values = −2

$$\text{Rate of Change} = \frac{\text{Change in } y\text{-values}}{\text{Change in } x\text{-values}} = \frac{-2}{+1} = -2$$

Linear Equation: $y = 6 - 2x$

EXAMPLE 2
SOLUTIONS
(CONTINUED)

b. Calculate the rate of change first when the start value is not given in the table.

x	y
−1	−2
1	8
4	23
6	33
9	48
12	63

Change in x-values = +2   Change in y-values = +10

$$\text{Rate of Change} = \frac{\text{Change in } y\text{-values}}{\text{Change in } x\text{-values}} = \frac{+10}{+2} = +5$$

To find the start value, use the rate of change to find the y-value that is paired with the x-value of 0.

x	y
−1	−2
0	3

+5

A rate of change of +5 means the y-value increases by 5 each time the x-value increases by 1. The x- and y-values one step before zero are given. Add 5 once to the y-value to get the start value: −2 + 5 = 3.

Linear Equation: $y = 3 + 5x$

EXERCISES

Write the equation for each recursive routine.

1. Rate of Change = +8
Start Value = −6

2. Rate of Change = $-\frac{1}{2}$
y-Intercept = $3\frac{1}{4}$

3. Rate of Change = +7.1
Start Value = 0

4. Rate of Change = −3
y-Intercept = 7

5. Start Value = −10
Rate of Change = 0

6. y-Intercept = 120
Rate of Change = −54

Determine the rate of change and y-intercept for each table. Write a linear equation that represents each table.

7.

x	y
0	4
1	12
2	20
3	28
4	36

8.

x	y
0	12
1	11
2	10
3	9
4	8

9.

x	y
−2	2
−1	4
0	6
1	8
3	12

Determine the rate of change and *y*-intercept for each table. Write a linear equation that represents each table.

10.

x	y
−1	29.5
0	31
3	35.5
4	37
7	41.5

11.

x	y
−2	−1
2	15
5	27
7	35
10	47

12.

x	y
4	1
6	2
10	4
13	5.5
18	8

13. Kirsten was able to finish 12 of her math homework problems at school. At home, she can do 4 problems every 2 minutes.

    a. How many problems does Kirsten complete each minute?
    b. What is Kirsten's start value for her homework on this particular day?
    c. Write a linear equation that represents this situation.
    d. What do the *x*-values represent in this equation?
    e. What do the *y*-values represent in this equation?

14. Jermaine wants to write a linear equation that will help him calculate how much money he has saved based on the number of days he has been saving. He begins with nothing in his savings. He saves $6 per day.
    a. What is the linear equation that represents this situation?
    b. How much will he have saved after 12 days?

15. Jack left a bottle of water sitting on the counter. When he first measured the temperature, it was 65° F. Each hour, he measured the temperature. It remained at 65° F.
    a. What is the *y*-intercept in this situation?
    b. What is the rate of change?
    c. Write a linear equation to represent the water's temperature based on the number of hours that have passed.

16. Shannon climbed to the top of a very tall slide and sent a ball down the slide. The top of the slide is 32 feet off the ground. The ball took only 4 seconds to make it to the bottom of the slide.
    a. What is the *y*-intercept in this situation?
    b. What is the rate of change in feet per second?
    c. Write a linear equation to represent the ball's height off the ground based on the number of seconds it has traveled.

Copy each table. Determine the rate of change and *y*-intercept. Fill in the missing values and write the linear equation that represents the table.

17.

x	y
0	−1
1	2
2	5
3	
4	

18.

x	y
−1	24
0	23.5
1	23
2	
3	

19.

x	y
0	14
1	25
2	36
5	
7	

Copy and complete each table by evaluating the given expression for the values listed.

20.

x	0.5x − 1	Output
−1		
0		
1		
2		
4		

21.

x	−2x + 7	Output
−2		
−1		
0		
3		
5		

Determine the rate of change for each situation.

22. $72 in 8 hours

23. 140 in 4 hours

24. 963 words in 9 minutes

25. 50 points for 4 assignments

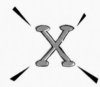

TIC-TAC-TOE ~ GEOMETRIC SEQUENCES

A geometric sequence is a list of numbers created by multiplying the previous term in the sequence by a common ratio. A geometric sequence can be described by a recursive routine with a start value and an operation. For example

Start Value = 4   Operation = × 2   Sequence: 4, 8, 16, 32, 64, …

Since geometric sequences are not linear, they will not be represented by the equation $y = b + mx$. Geometric sequences can be represented by the equation $y = b \cdot m^x$ where b is the start value and m is the amount used for the repeated multiplication. For the example above, an equation to represent this sequence is $y = 4 \cdot 2^x$.

Copy and complete each geometric sequence. Give the start value and the operation.

1. 5, 15, _____, 135, _____

2. 2, −4, _____, −16, 32, _____

3. 120, _____, 30, 15, _____

4. −100, 10, _____, _____, _____

5. Find the 8th term in each geometric sequence in **Exercises #1 through #4**.

6. Write an equation to represent each geometric sequence in **#1-4**.

7. Create two of your own geometric sequences. Record the start value, operation and the tenth term. Write an equation representing each sequence.

INPUT - OUTPUT TABLES FROM EQUATIONS

Determine the rate of change and start value from linear equations.
Create input-output tables from linear equations.

The Commutative Property of Addition states that numbers can be added in any order. This can be applied in a linear equation. In **Lesson 12**, linear equations were shown in the form $y = b + mx$. Based on the Commutative Property, this equation can also be written $y = mx + b$. For example:

$$y = 7 + 2x \rightarrow y = 2x + 7$$
$$y = 4 - 3x \rightarrow y = -3x + 4$$

Notice that the "−" belongs to the rate of change and must move with it.

EXPLORE!

LINEAR QUALITIES

Use the linear equations given in the box to complete this activity.

Step 1: List the equation(s) that have a negative rate of change.

Step 2: List the equations(s) that have a positive y-intercept.

Step 3: Which equation has a start value of zero? How do you know?

Step 4: Which equation has a rate of change equal to zero? How do you know?

Step 5: Create your own linear equation that fits the given description.
    a. A positive start value and negative rate of change.
    b. A rate of change equal to zero.
    c. A start value equal to zero.
    d. A negative rate of change and a negative y-intercept.

$$y = 2 - 3x$$
$$y = -5$$
$$y = 4x - 9$$
$$y = -7 + \tfrac{1}{2}x$$
$$y = -6x + 1$$
$$y = 2x$$
$$y = 8 + x$$

There are times when you are given the equation that describes a relationship between two pieces of information. An equation is useful in creating other ways to display the information. The most common ways of displaying data are through graphs, tables and words.

Over summer break Josie went to the mall with her friends. At noon, they left the mall and began walking. The equation $y = 2 + 3x$ represents Josie's distance (y) from her home. The x represents the number of hours she has walked.

If Josie walked for at least three hours, an input-output table of values can be created that shows how far Josie is from home based on how long she has been walking. This can be done by identifying the *y*-intercept and rate of change of the situation.

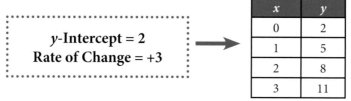

y-Intercept = 2
Rate of Change = +3

x	*y*
0	2
1	5
2	8
3	11

Graphs are another way to visually display equations. Take each ordered pair from the table and graph it on a coordinate plane. Since Josie is continually walking, the points can be connected to form a straight line.

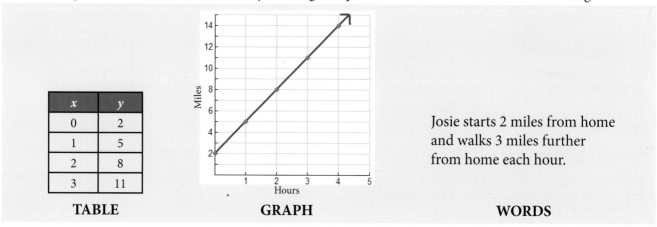

x	*y*
0	2
1	5
2	8
3	11

TABLE

GRAPH

Josie starts 2 miles from home and walks 3 miles further from home each hour.

WORDS

Input-output tables can be completed by evaluating the equation for the values given in the table.

EXAMPLE 1

Use the linear equation to complete the input-output table. $y = 3x + 8$

x	*y*
−4	
7	
16	
29	

SOLUTION

Substitute each *x*-value into the equation to determine the *y*-values.

x	3*x* + 8	*y*
−4	3(−4) + 8	−4
7	3(7) + 8	29
16	3(16) + 8	56
29	3(29) + 8	95

Any input-output table can be turned into ordered pairs and graphed. When dealing with linear equations, graphing is a great way to double-check the calculations as all points should be in a straight line.

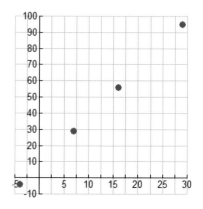

EXERCISES

Determine the rate of change and the *y*-intercept from the given equations.

1. $y = 8 + 2x$

2. $y = 3x - 11$

3. $y = x - 4$

4. $y = 5 - 4x$

5. $y = -\frac{1}{4}x$

6. $y = -1$

7. $y = \frac{2}{3}x - 8$

8. $y = 6$

9. $y = 2 - \frac{4}{7}x$

Given the equation, copy and complete the input-output tables.

10. $y = 2x - 3$

x	2x – 3	y
0		
3		
9		
10		
13		

11. $y = x + 9$

x	x + 9	y
–4		
0		
2		
5		
21		

12. $y = -10 + 6x$

x	–10 + 6x	y
–7		
–3		
1		
4		
15		

13. $y = -3x$

x	y
–3	
–1	
6	
10	
20	

14. $y = \frac{1}{2}x + 1$

x	y
–6	
–1	
4	
6	
11	

15. $y = 5$

x	y
–4	
–3	
0	
1	
5	

16. Gracie planted a marigold in June. She measured its height each week and found that the height of the plant could be represented by the equation $y = 3 + 0.5x$ where *x* represents the number of weeks that have passed and *y* represents the height of the plant in inches.

   a. Copy and complete the table to show the height of the marigold through the summer.

x	y
0	
4	
7	
10	
12	

   b. Graph the ordered pairs on a coordinate plane.

17. Star is able to run 6.8 meters per second when she is sprinting. She wants to figure out how many meters (y) she can run based on the number of seconds (x) she has run. She developed an equation to help her: $y = 6.8x$.

x seconds	y meters run
10	
25	
40	
60	
100	

   a. Copy and complete the table using Star's equation.
   b. Four hundred meters is approximately a quarter of a mile. About how long would it take Star to run one-quarter of a mile? Is this reasonable? Why or why not?
   c. Star decides she is going to run for one hour. How many seconds is this?
   d. According to her equation, how many meters would she run in one hour?
   e. How many miles is this? 1 mile ≈ 1,600 meters
   f. Is this answer reasonable? Why or why not?

18. During the summer, Jorge works at a kids camp. He was given $100 for signing on for the summer and then is paid an additional $35 per day of work. The linear equation that represents Jorge's total earnings is $y = 100 + 35x$. Copy and complete the table that shows Jorge's total earnings based on how many days he works.

x days	y earnings
6	
20	
32	
44	
50	

REVIEW

Solve each equation. Check your solution.

19. $2x + 7 = 22$

20. $\frac{x}{5} - 9 = -3$

21. $-x + 2 = 8$

22. $4(x + 7) = 12$

23. $6x + 1 = 5x + 4$

24. $2(3x - 2) = 38$

25. $2x - 5 = 5x + 28$

26. $6 + \frac{x}{3} = 2$

27. $8 = 23 - 5x$

TIC-TAC-TOE ~ WRITING EQUATIONS FROM TABLES

Creating equations from input-output tables is a difficult process. Create a worksheet that steps a student through the process of finding the rate of change, the start value and then writing the equation. Include tables that have a start value listed in the table and some that do not. Turn in a blank copy of the worksheet and an answer key.

CALCULATING SLOPE FROM GRAPHS

LESSON 14

Use slope triangles to find the slope of lines.

Up to this point you have looked at linear relationships by examining their rates of change and start values which are also called *y*-intercepts. The rate of change tells you how much the *y*-value should increase or decrease as the counter (*x*) increases.

Rate of change is also known as slope. Like rate of change, slope is used to describe the steepness of a line. Slope is the ratio of the vertical change (the rise) to the horizontal change (the run). The easiest way to calculate the slope of a line when it is graphed is to create a slope triangle. A slope triangle is formed by drawing a right triangle where one leg of the triangle represents the vertical rise and the other leg is the horizontal run. The hypotenuse of the triangle (the longest side) is part of the line itself. Start at the point furthest to the left and go up or down to draw your first leg. Then draw your second leg to the right.

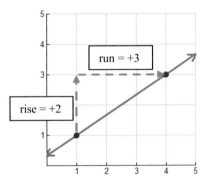

$$\text{Slope} = \frac{\text{rise}}{\text{run}} = \frac{+2}{+3} = \frac{2}{3}$$

A line can have a slope that is positive, negative, zero or undefined.

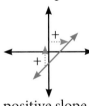

positive slope

negative slope

zero slope

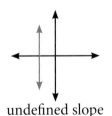

undefined slope

FINDING SLOPE

The slope of a line is the ratio of the change in *y*-values to the change in *x*-values.

$$\text{Slope} = \text{Rate of Change} = \frac{\text{Change in } y\text{-values}}{\text{Change in } x\text{-values}} = \frac{\text{rise}}{\text{run}}$$

EXAMPLE 1

Draw a slope triangle for each line (when possible) and identify the slope of the line.

a.
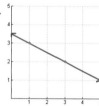

b.

c.
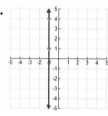

d.
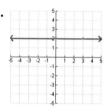

SOLUTIONS

a.
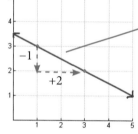

$$\text{Slope} = \frac{\text{rise}}{\text{run}} = -\frac{-1}{+2} = -\frac{1}{2}$$

b.
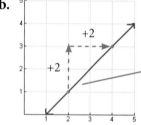

$$\text{Slope} = \frac{\text{rise}}{\text{run}} = \frac{+2}{+2} = 1$$

c.
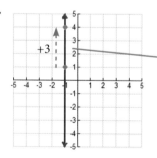

$$\text{Slope} = \frac{\text{rise}}{\text{run}} = \frac{+3}{0} = \text{undefined}$$

d.
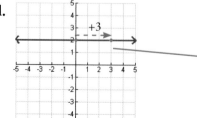

$$\text{Slope} = \frac{\text{rise}}{\text{run}} = \frac{0}{+3} = 0$$

There are times when a graph is not provided. You may only be given a table of values or two ordered pairs. In each of these situations, you can graph the points and then create a slope triangle to calculate the slope.

EXAMPLE 2

Graph the line that goes through the given points, draw a slope triangle and give the slope.

a.

x	y
2	7
5	1

b. **(0, 1) and (2, 4)**

SOLUTIONS

a. Graph the points.

Draw the slope triangle. Start at the point furthest to the left.

Determine the lengths of the legs of the triangle.
Slope $= \dfrac{\text{rise}}{\text{run}} = \dfrac{-6}{+3} = -2$

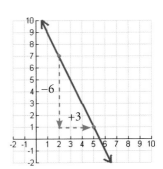

b. Graph the points.

Draw the slope triangle. Start at the point furthest to the left.

Determine the lengths of the legs of the triangle.
Slope $= \dfrac{\text{rise}}{\text{run}} = \dfrac{+3}{+2} = \dfrac{3}{2}$

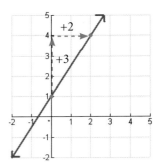

When given the slope of a linear relationship you can draw a line that has the given slope using rise over run. When a slope is written without a denominator, it is mathematically correct to place a 1 in the denominator. This does not change the value of the slope. For example:

$$3 \rightarrow \dfrac{3}{1}$$

EXAMPLE 3

Graph a line with a slope of 2.

SOLUTION

No y-intercept was given so put a point anywhere on the graph.

The slope of 2 can be written as $\dfrac{2}{1}$.

From the point, rise +2 and run +1.

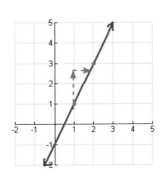

EXERCISES

Find the slope of each line.

1.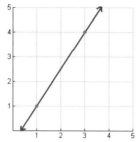

2.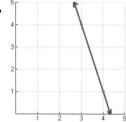

3.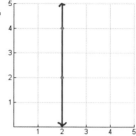

4.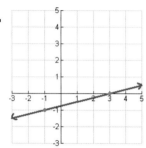

5.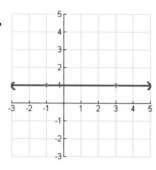

6.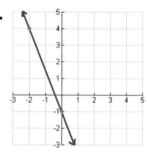

Use each table or graph to determine if the slope of the line is positive, negative, zero or undefined.

7.

x	y
0	12
1	9
2	6
3	3

8.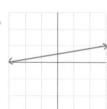

9.

x	y
4	7
7	7
12	7
16	7

10.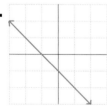

11.

x	y
−3	1
−1	3
3	7
6	10

12.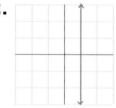

13. Karissa and Rider both calculated the slope of the same line. Rider says the slope is $\frac{-2}{3}$ and Karissa believes the slope is $\frac{2}{-3}$.

    a. On a coordinate plane, graph a line that goes through the origin and has a slope of $\frac{-2}{3}$.

    b. On a different coordinate plane, graph a line that goes through the origin and has a slope of $\frac{2}{-3}$.

    c. What do you notice about the two lines? The teacher says the slope is $-\frac{2}{3}$. Is this the same slope as found by Karissa, Rider or both?

On a coordinate plane, graph a line with the given slope.

14. slope = $\frac{3}{4}$

15. slope = −3

16. slope = 0

Draw each line through the given point that has the given slope on a coordinate plane. Name one other ordered pair that is on the line.

17. (1, 3) slope = −2

18. (−2, 1), slope = $-\frac{2}{5}$

19. (3, −4), slope = undefined

20. Barry is building a staircase from the first floor to the second floor. The height between the two floors is 12 feet. He wants the slope of the stairs to be $\frac{4}{3}$. What is the horizontal distance that the stairs will cover?

21. A wheel chair ramp is being designed for the library entrance. The pavement pouring company advises that the slope of the ramp be $\frac{2}{7}$. If the entrance to the library is 6 feet above ground, how long will the ramp need to be?

22. When finding the slope of a line on a graph, can you choose any two points on the line? Prove the answer by determining the slope of the line shown at the right using three different slope triangles.

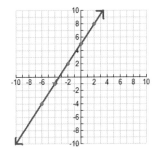

REVIEW

Evaluate each expression using the order of operations. Write all answers in simplest form.

23. $\frac{7-3}{12-6}$

24. $\frac{-1-8}{6-3}$

25. $\frac{4-(-5)}{4-3}$

26. $\frac{8-8}{1-7}$

27. $\frac{7-2}{5-5}$

28. $\frac{-3-(-2)}{7-(-10)}$

TIC-TAC-TOE ~ CHILDREN'S STORY

Sequences occur in many real-world situations. Create a children's book that incorporates the concept of recursive sequences and recursive routines. The character(s) in your book should encounter sequences in a variety of real-world situations. The plot should include the character(s) needing to find the start values, operations and specific term in recursive sequences. Your book should have a cover, illustrations and a story line that is appropriate for children.

THE SLOPE FORMULA

Find the slope of a line using the slope formula.

EXPLORE!   **FIND THAT FORMULA**

Ginger got a job in downtown Portland. She bought a parking pass at a garage not far from her place of work. The table shows her total parking expenses based on the number of weeks she has been parking at the garage.

Week x	Total Expenses, y
6	$50
10	$74
12	$86
24	$158

Step 1: Calculate the rate of change (the change in *y* over the change in *x*) for the table above.

Step 2: Graph the ordered pairs on a Quadrant I coordinate plane like the one shown below. Draw a line through the points

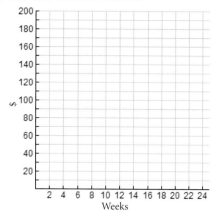

Step 3: Make a slope triangle and determine the slope of the line.

Step 4: What do you notice about the rate of change and the slope of the line?

Step 5: If you were given the table of values in the table at right, what would the rate of change (or slope) ratio look like?

x	y
x_1	y_1
x_2	y_2

Step 6: The ratio developed in **Step 5** is called the "Slope Formula". The subscripts identify two different points. Try your formula on these points from the table above: (6, 50) and (12, 86). Did you get the same slope as you did in **Steps 1 and 3**?

Step 7: You have learned three methods for finding slope: rate of change, slope triangles and the slope formula. Which method do you like the best? Why?

THE SLOPE FORMULA

The formula for the slope of a line that goes through a point with coordinates (x_1, y_1) and another point with coordinates (x_2, y_2) is

$$\text{Slope} = \frac{y_2 - y_1}{x_2 - x_1}$$

Subscripts designate which point you are using in your calculation. You read x_1 as "x sub one". Think of it as saying "the x-coordinate of the first point".

EXAMPLE 1

Use the slope formula to find the slope of each line that passes through the given points.
a. (3, 2) and (8, 5)
b. (1, −1) and (3, −5)
c. (6, −2) and (6, 4)

> Sometimes it helps to write the subscript letters over your points to stay organized:
> $$\overset{x_1 \; y_1}{(3, 2)}$$

SOLUTIONS

a. Let (3, 2) be (x_1, y_1) and (8, 5) be (x_2, y_2).
Substitute the numbers into the slope formula.

$$\frac{y_2 - y_1}{x_2 - x_1}$$

$$\frac{5 - 2}{8 - 3} = \frac{3}{5}$$

b. Let (1, −1) be (x_1, y_1) and (3, −5) be (x_2, y_2).
Substitute the numbers into the slope formula.

$$\frac{y_2 - y_1}{x_2 - x_1}$$

$$\frac{-5 - (-1)}{3 - 1} = \frac{-4}{2} = -2$$

> It is impossible to divide by 0 so the slope is undefined.

c. Let (6, −2) be (x_1, y_1) and (6, 4) be (x_2, y_2).
Substitute the numbers into the slope formula.

$$\frac{y_2 - y_1}{x_2 - x_1}$$

$$\frac{4 - (-2)}{6 - 6} = \frac{6}{0} = \text{undefined}$$

You have learned three methods for calculating slope. All three methods will work in any situation. Depending on the way the linear relationship is presented, there may be one method that is easier than the other two methods.

RATE OF CHANGE   Easiest method when information is presented in an input-output table.

SLOPE TRIANGLE   Easiest method when information is presented in a graph.

SLOPE FORMULA   Easiest method when given two ordered pairs.

EXERCISES

Find the slope of the line that passes through the given points.

1. (4, 7) and (6, 10)

2. (0, 8) and (3, 5)

3. (−1, 11) and (4, 11)

4. (−6, −1) and (2, 0)

5. (7, −2) and (7, 9)

6. (6, 4) and (2, 10)

7. (−2, 10) and (3, 10)

8. (0, −4) and (5, 0)

9. (9, 8) and (4, 18)

10. In each part below, explain what method you would choose to calculate the slope. Then find the slope.

a.

x	y
2	2
5	11
9	23
14	38

b. A line through (1, 5) and (−2, 9)

c.

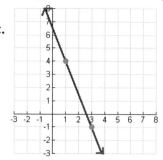

11. Consider the line through the points (3, 8) and (8, 12).
   a. Find the slope.
   b. Convert your slope fraction to a decimal. Remember that this is your rate of change.
   c. The rate of change tells you how much to increase or decrease for every one-unit step. Copy and complete the table using the rate of change.
   d. How many ordered pairs for this line do you have now? How many more could you figure out?

x	y
3	8
4	
5	
6	
7	
8	12

12. Tanika joined a gym. At 4 months, she had paid a total of $94 in membership fees. After 9 months, she had paid a total of $204 in membership fees. Let x represent the number of months she has been a member and y represent the total she has paid in membership fees.
   a. Write two ordered pairs to represent Tanika's gym membership information.
   b. Find the slope of the line that contains the two points in **part a**.
   c. The slope represents the rate of change in real-world situations. What does the slope represent in terms of Tanika's gym membership fee?

13. Scott skis at Willamette Pass during the winter. His favorite run has a vertical descent of 1,560 feet. The run covers a horizontal distance of 3,900 feet. What is the slope of this particular run? Give the answer as a fraction and as a decimal.

14. Devin drove up a hill. After he drove 4 minutes, he was at an elevation of 620 feet. After he drove 12 minutes he was 1,580 feet high.
   a. Should the x-values represent minutes or feet? Why?
   b. Calculate the rate of change in this situation. What method did you use and why?
   c. If he continues to climb at this rate, how much elevation will he gain in the next 15 minutes?

15. Nigel put a two-liter bottle of soda in his locker. He did not realize there was a hole in the bottom of the container and that the liquid had slowly dripped out. The graph represents the amount of soda left in the bottle based on the amount of time that had passed.

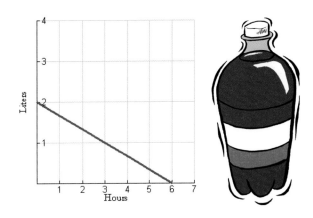

    a. What is the slope of the line?

    b. What does the value of the slope represent in this situation?

    c. How many hours had passed when Nigel's soda bottle became empty?

REVIEW

Match each recursive rule with its linear equation.

16. Start Value: 4   Slope: $\frac{1}{2}$

17. Start Value: −2   Rate of Change: $+\frac{1}{2}$

18. y-Intercept: 1   Slope: 3

19. Start Value: $\frac{1}{2}$ Rate of Change: −2

20. y-Intercept: 3   Rate of Change: +1

21. Start Value: −2   Slope: 0

22. y-Intercept: 0   Rate of Change: +2

A. $y = 3x + 1$

B. $y = \frac{1}{2} - 2x$

C. $y = 2x$

D. $y = x + 3$

E. $y = 4 + \frac{1}{2}x$

F. $y = \frac{1}{2}x - 2$

G. $y = -2$

TIC-TAC-TOE ~ SLOPE METHODS

You have learned to find the slope of a line when given either a graph, table or two ordered pairs. Create a flip book that explains how to use the slope formula, slope triangles and input-output tables to find slope. Include examples and diagrams.

Finding Slope

Vocabulary

function	recursive routine	slope
linear equation	recursive sequence	slope triangle
rate of change		y-intercept

Write recursive routines and create recursive sequences.
Create linear plots for recursive sequences.
Represent recursive routine applications with graphs, tables and words.
Calculate rates of change and start values.
Write linear equations from recursive routines.
Determine the rate of change and start value from linear equations.
Create input-output tables from linear equations.
Use slope triangles to find the slope of lines.
Find the slope of a line using the slope formula.

Lesson 8 ~ Recursive Routines

• •

Copy each sequence of numbers and fill in the missing values. Identify the start value and the operation that must be performed to arrive at the next term.

1. 8, 1, –6, _____, _____, _____

2. 92, 110, _____, 146, _____, _____

3. 7, 7.6, _____, _____, 9.4, _____

4. _____, _____, 19, 22, 25, _____

For each sequence below, describe the recursive routine (start value and operation) and give the 9th term in the sequence.

5. 18, 5, –8, –21, …

6. $\frac{2}{5}$, $\frac{4}{5}$, $1\frac{1}{5}$, $1\frac{3}{5}$, …

7. Draw the next two figures in the following pattern. Each block is 1unit by 1 unit.

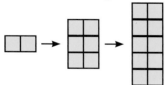

    a. What is the perimeter of the first figure?
    b. What is the perimeter of the second figure? The third figure?
    c. Write the recursive routine (start value and operation) that describes the perimeters.
    d. Predict the perimeter of the seventh figure in this pattern.

Lesson 9 ~ Linear Plots

• •

Describe the linear relationship given by the *y*-coordinates on each linear plot below by stating the start value and operation. Create an input-output table showing the ordered pairs represented by each plot.

8.

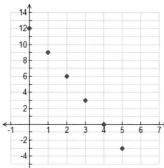

9.

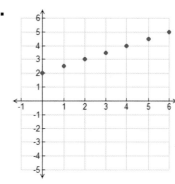

10. Create a linear plot for the first five ordered pairs in the given recursive routine describing the *y*-coordinates.

    a. Start Value: 11

       Operation: Subtract 2

    b. Start Value: − 4

       Operation: Add $\frac{1}{2}$

Lesson 10 ~ Recursive Routine Applications

• •

11. Determine an appropriate range for the *y*-axis and state what increments should be used on the graph.

a.

Hours	Miles Traveled
0	55
1	110
2	165
3	220
4	275

b.

Years	Savings
0	$10,200
1	$9,400
2	$8,600
3	$7,800
4	$7,000

12. LaQuisha borrows $150 from her parents to buy school clothes. Each week she uses $12 of her allowance to repay her parents.

    a. Write a recursive routine that describes LaQuisha's balance based on the number of weeks that have passed since she borrowed the money.

    b. Fill in an input-ouput table that will give her balance for 0 to 5 weeks.

    c. Create a linear plot that shows LaQuisha's balance through the first five weeks.

     d. Use your calculator to determine how many weeks it will take before LaQuisha has repaid her parents. How much was her last payment?

13. In Oregon, the cost of a gallon of gasoline in April 2008 averaged $3.35. One analyst predicted that the cost of gas would rise $0.40 per year.

    a. Write a recursive routine that describes the price of gasoline based on the number of years that have passed since April 2008.

    b. Create an input-output table for the value of a gallon of gas for 0 to 5 years. Let 2008 represent year 0.

    c. Create a linear plot that shows the cost of a gallon of gasoline through the first five years.

    d. Determine how many years it will take before the cost of gasoline will be over $10 per gallon according to this analyst's prediction.

Lesson 11 ~ Rate of Change

Determine the rate of change for each situation.

14. Jordan collected 28 coins in 4 days.

15. Rebecca drove 270 miles in 6 hours.

16. Shea spent $4.56 for 12 doughnuts.

Determine the rate of change and start value for each table.

17.

x	y
0	2
1	9
2	16
3	23
4	30

18.

x	y
0	33
3	0
5	−22
6	−33
8	−55

19.

x	y
−1	9
1	17
3	25
5	33
8	45

20. Maria began an exercise plan at the beginning of the school year. In the table shown below, Maria records her weight at different points during the school year. Assume Maria loses the same amount every week.

    a. How many pounds is Maria losing each week?

    b. How much did she weigh when she first started this exercise plan?

Weeks Since Maria Started Exercising	Her Weight
1	161
5	153
7	149
10	143

    c. If this pattern continues, how much will she weigh 17 weeks into her exercise plan?

    d. Does it make sense that this pattern will continue throughout the whole school year? Why or why not?

Write the linear equation for each recursive rule.

21. Rate of Change = +6
Start Value = −2

22. Rate of Change = $-\frac{1}{2}$
y-Intercept = 6

23. Rate of Change = +3.8
Start Value = 1

Determine the rate of change and y-intercept for each table. Write a linear equation that represents each table.

24.

x	y
0	39
1	33
2	27
3	21
4	15

25.

x	y
−2	2.9
−1	6.4
0	9.9
1	13.4
3	20.4

26.

x	y
−2	−15
2	1
5	13
7	21
10	33

27. Madison receives $42 at the beginning of the month to use for lunch money. Each day at school she buys the lunch special and a milk. This costs her $3.10. Madison wants to develop a linear equation to calculate how much money she has left based on the number of days she has bought lunch during a month.

   a. What is the y-intercept in this situation?
   b. What is the rate of change?
   c. Write a linear equation to represent the amount of lunch money Madison has left based on the number of days this month she has bought lunch.

Lesson 13 ~ Input-Output Tables from Equations

Determine the rate of change and the y-intercept from the given equations.

28. $y = 5x + 1$

29. $y = 7 − 6x$

30. $y = 2 + \frac{1}{2}x$

31. $y = 2x + 7$

32. $y = \frac{2}{9}x$

33. $y = 8$

Given the equation, copy and complete the input-output tables.

34. $y = 3x + 1$

x	y
0	
3	
9	
10	
13	

35. $y = \frac{1}{3}x + 4$

x	y
0	
3	
4	
6	
11	

36. $y = 8x + 7$

x	y
−7	
−3	
1	
4	
15	

Find the slope of each line.

37.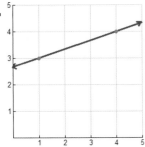

38.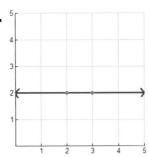

39.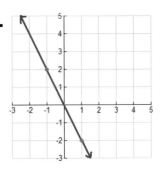

Create a coordinate plane, draw a line through the given point that has the given slope. Name one other ordered pair that is on the line.

40. $(0, 0)$, slope $= \frac{1}{2}$

41. $(-1, 3)$, slope $= -4$

42. $(0, 2)$, slope $= 0$

43. A ladder leaned against a wall at a slope of $\frac{4}{3}$. The top of the ladder was 12 feet off the ground. How far is the bottom of the ladder from the base of the wall?

44. The ladder in **Exercise 43** is leaning against another wall only 10 feet off the ground. The bottom of the ladder is 10 feet away from the base of the building.
   a. What is the slope of the ladder in this position?
   b. Is it steeper than the slope of the ladder in **Exercise 43**? Why or why not?

Lesson 15 ~ The Slope Formula

Find the slope of the line that passes through the given points.

45. $(3, 2)$ and $(6, 6)$

46. $(0, 5)$ and $(3, 8)$

47. $(-2, 9)$ and $(8, 9)$

48. $(3, -2)$ and $(5, -5)$

49. $(3, 2)$ and $(3, 4)$

50. $(7, 5)$ and $(3, 11)$

51. For each part below, explain which method you would choose to calculate the slope. Then find the slope.

a.

x	y
2	21
6	13
9	7
11	3

b. A line through $(3, 6)$ and $(-1, 11)$

c.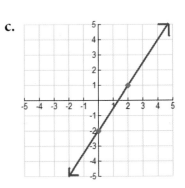

52. Angelina's family planned to rent a vacation home in Sunriver, Oregon. For 3 nights it would cost a total of $510. For 5 nights it would cost a total of $800. Let *x* represent the number of nights the house would be rented and *y* represent the total cost.

a. Write two ordered pairs to represent the house rental information.

b. Find the slope of the line that contains the two points in **part a**.

c. The slope represents the rate of change in real-world situations. What does your slope represent in terms of Angelina's house rental?

TIC-TAC-TOE ~ SIMILAR SLOPE TRIANGLES

Use graph paper to draw three coordinate planes each from −10 to 10 on both axes.

Step 1: On the first coordinate plane, draw a line with a slope of $\frac{2}{3}$.

Step 2: Draw three different sizes of slope triangles on the line. For example, the graph below shows three different slope triangles for a line with a slope of $-\frac{1}{3}$.

Step 3: Write the slope fraction for each triangle.

Step 4: What do you notice about the slope fractions?

Step 5: On the second coordinate plane, draw a line with a slope of −2. On the third coordinate plane, draw a line with a slope of $\frac{1}{4}$. Repeat **Steps 2-4** for these two graphs.

Step 6: Can you draw any size of slope triangle on a line and get the correct slope? Are all slope triangles drawn on a given line similar? Summarize your results. Use math to support your answers.

KAREN
NEWSPAPER CITY EDITOR
ALBANY, OREGON

I am an editor for a daily newspaper. Our paper has a circulation of about 17,000. I coordinate local news coverage and oversee a staff of seven reporters. I also edit stories, decide when and where stories will run and design the local pages. Most of my time is spent working with the reporters on stories and laying out how each page will look. I also respond to telephone calls and emails from the public. Other duties include overseeing a monthly special section on homes and gardens and leading staff meetings twice a month.

Math is part of my job in at least a small way every day. I use ratios and percentages to figure out how articles and pictures of varying sizes fit into a given space. I approve time cards and expense reports so I need to double check the figures for correct addition and multiplication. Statistics are an important element of many news stories. I make sure numbers in the stories are correct and logical for the situation. For example, our paper may do a story on how crime has changed over the past three years. This might include overall figures, a breakdown of crime totals and percentages showing the increases or decreases from prior years. It might also compare types of crimes. The first thing I do is double check the figures to make sure the reported values correspond to the text. Secondly, if the story says overall crime is down but property crime is on the rise, the numbers we print had better show that fact.

I received a Master of Arts degree in journalism. I also have a bachelor's degree in Biology, though most people in my profession have degrees in journalism, writing or English. Salaries depend on where you work (the size of the city) as well as experience. A typical starting salary for a beginning copy editor is around $20,000 per year. A beginning city editor might start around $30,000 per year. An executive editor earns $50,000 per year or more.

Creating a newspaper is exciting. There is the pressure of deadlines, the challenge of editing, the creativity of page design and the sense of accomplishment that comes each day when you flip through the paper that you created. There is great satisfaction creating a product every day and knowing you did your best to make it meaningful for the thousands of people it reaches.

BLOCK 3 ~ LINEAR EQUATIONS

USING LINEAR EQUATIONS

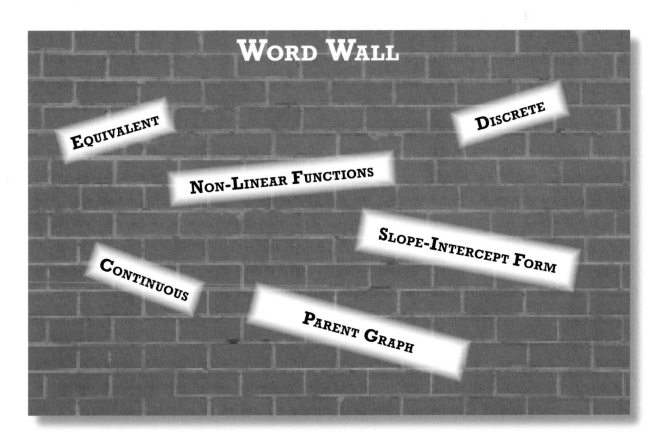

BLOCK 3 ~ USING LINEAR EQUATIONS
TIC - TAC - TOE

X- AND *Y*-INTERCEPTS

Graph linear equations in standard form using the *x*- and *y*-intercepts.

See page 97 for details.

CLASS COMPETITION

Create a class competition where participants graph and write linear equations.

See page 112 for details.

GRAPHING DESIGN

Graph many linear equations to create an artistic design.

See page 103 for details.

CAREERS USING ALGEBRA

Research and write a report about different career choices where knowledge of algebra is essential.

See page 116 for details.

PARALLEL OR PERPENDICULAR LINES

Graph parallel and perpendicular lines. Make predictions about the slopes of the lines.

See page 103 for details.

QUADRATIC FUNCTIONS

Graph quadratic functions in factored form.

See page 122 for details.

EXPONENTIAL EQUATIONS

Use the exponential equation to predict future amounts.

See page 117 for details.

EQUIVALENT EQUATIONS

Make a flap book which matches pairs of equivalent linear equations.

See page 112 for details.

LINES OF BEST FIT

Draw lines of best fit, find equations and make predictions.

See page 108 for details.

GRAPHING USING SLOPE - INTERCEPT FORM

LESSON 16

 Graph linear equations in slope-intercept form.

In **Lesson 12** you were introduced to linear functions. **Slope-intercept form** is the most common equation used to represent a linear function. It is called this because the slope and the y-intercept are easily identified.

> ### SLOPE-INTERCEPT FORM OF A LINEAR EQUATION
> $$y = mx + b$$
> The slope of the line is represented by m.
> The y-intercept is b.

- Slope (m) is also called the rate of change. The slope gives you the rise over the run of the line.

- The y-intercept is also called the start value. The y-intercept is the location the line crosses the y-axis. The ordered pair for the y-intercept will be $(0, b)$.

- Equations in slope-intercept form may also be written $y = b + mx$.

Graphing an equation is a very important skill in mathematics because it is a visual representation of a mathematical equation. In this lesson you will learn how to graph an equation when it is presented in slope-intercept form.

EXAMPLE 1

Graph $y = \frac{1}{3}x - 2$. **Clearly mark at least three points on the line.**

SOLUTION

First determine the slope and y-intercept. $y = \frac{1}{3}x - 2$ ← y-intercept
$m = \frac{1}{3}$ and $b = -2$ ↖ slope

| Start by graphing the y-intercept on the coordinate plane. | Use the slope to find at least two more points. Remember rise over run. | Draw a straight line through the points. Put an arrow on each end. |

EXAMPLE 2

Graph each linear equation. Clearly mark at least three points on each line.

a. $y = 6 - 2x$ b. $y = -\frac{7}{2}x + 1$

SOLUTIONS

a. $y = 6 - 2x \rightarrow m = -2$ and $b = 6$

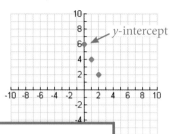

The slope is the coefficient of x.

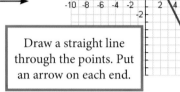

y-intercept

Graph the *y*-intercept of 6 and then graph 3 points using the slope fraction $-2 = \frac{-2}{1}$.

Draw a straight line through the points. Put an arrow on each end.

b. $y = -\frac{7}{2}x + 1 \rightarrow m = -\frac{7}{2} = \frac{-7}{2}$ and $b = 1$

Put the negative in either the numerator or the denominator.

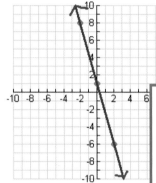

Sometimes you may have to use your slope in two directions. Go down 7 and right 2. In order to get another point on the coordinate plane, go up 7 and left 2.

$$\frac{-7}{2} = \frac{7}{-2}$$

As you learned in **Block 2**, there are lines that have a slope of zero and other lines that have an undefined slope. The equations of these lines are unique.

Zero Slope
$y = $ constant

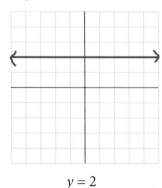

$y = 2$

Undefined Slope
$x = $ constant

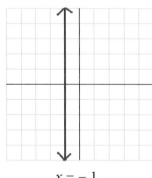

$x = -1$

When a graph can be drawn from beginning to end without lifting your pencil, it is **continuous**. Some situations are modeled by linear equations but are not continuous. This could mean that it would not make sense to connect the points of the equation with a line.

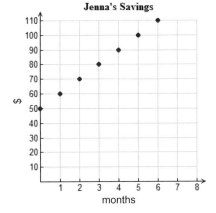

Jenna's Savings

For example, Jenna started with $50 in her savings account. She adds $10 each month. The linear equation that represents the balance in her savings account is $y = 50 + 10x$. Since she only puts money in her account once a month, a line should not be drawn through the points on the graph. Only the whole numbers and 0 can be used as x-values. This graph is called **discrete** because it is represented by a unique set of points rather than a continuous line.

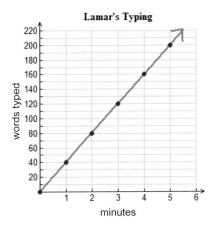

Lamar's Typing

A graph can be continuous but limited to a certain quadrant or section of the graph. For example, Lamar types 40 words per minute. It would not make sense to graph points out of the first quadrant because he cannot type for a negative number of minutes or type a negative number of words. This graph is continuous because it can be drawn without lifting your pencil.

EXERCISES

Draw a coordinate plane for each problem. Graph the given equation. Clearly mark three points on the line.

1. $y = \frac{1}{2}x - 3$

2. $y = 1 - 3x$

3. $y = -\frac{2}{5}x + 6$

4. $y = x + 2$

5. $y = 4$

6. $y = -5 + \frac{4}{3}x$

7. $x = -2$

8. $y = 5x$

9. $y = -\frac{3}{2}x + 4$

10. Taylor's graphs of two different linear equations are seen below. His teacher told him both graphs were incorrect. Explain to Taylor, in complete sentences, why each of his graphs is not correct.

a. $y = \frac{4}{5}x + 1$

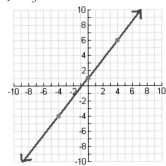

b. $x = 3$

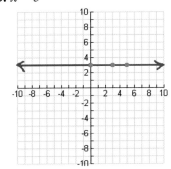

11. Daryl was given the linear equation $y = 1.5x + 2$. He was not sure how to graph this equation because its slope was a decimal. Follow the process Daryl decided to use.

x	y
−2	
0	
2	
4	

    a. Copy the table and use the equation to fill in the output values.
    b. Graph your ordered pairs (x, y) from the table on a coordinate plane. Draw a line through the points.
    c. Daryl was quite happy with the graph of the linear equation and was sure he had found the easiest way to deal with a linear equation which has a decimal slope value. Do you agree with him? Why or why not?

12. Graph the three linear equations on the same coordinate plane. In complete sentences, describe the similarities and differences of the three lines.

    $y = \frac{3}{4}x$ $y = \frac{3}{4}x - 5$ $y = \frac{3}{4}x + 2$

13. Create a linear equation that satisfies each condition. Graph your equations on a coordinate plane.
    a. Slope $= \frac{1}{3}$ and a negative y-intercept
    b. Slope $= 0$ and a y-intercept of 4
    c. A positive slope and a positive y-intercept
    d. A negative slope and a y-intercept of 0.

14. Mrs. Samuels warned her class that the linear equations shown below were the most-often missed problems on the linear equations test she gave to her class last year. Explain why you think each problem might have been missed and then graph each equation.
    a. $y = x - 3$
    b. $y = 4$
    c. $x = -4$
    d. $y = 6 - x$

15. Falls City, Oregon experienced a massive rainstorm from December 26th to December 30th in 1936. On the first day of the storm it rained 5.5 inches. It continued to rain 2.5 inches each day for the next four days.

x	y
1	
2	
3	
4	
5	

    a. Fill in the table with the TOTAL rain that had fallen during the storm as each day passed.
    b. In this situation, which number represents the slope (or rate of change)?
    c. Determine the y-intercept.
    d. Write a linear equation that represents the total rainfall in Falls City based on the number of days the storm has lasted.
    e. If the storm had continued at the same rate for 10 days, what would have been the total rainfall?

16. Dave was able to do 3 pull-ups before attending PE class. Each week of PE, the number of pull-ups he was able to do increased by 2.
    a. Write a linear equation representing the number of pull-ups, y, Dave was able to do in a given week, x.
    b. Would this graph be a continuous line? Why or why not?
    c. Graph the equation in the way that best models the situation.

Choose which of the following graphs is the best model for each situation. Explain your reasoning.

A. 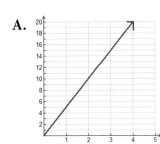 B. 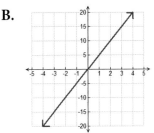 C.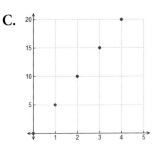

17. Ima started collecting coins. She adds 5 coins to her collection each week.

18. Todd runs at a rate of 5 miles per hour.

19. A continuous relationship where y is 5 times x.

REVIEW

Find the slope of the line that passes through the given points.

20. (2, 9) and (6, 11)

21. (1, 2) and (1, 6)

22. (3, −1) and (5, 0)

23. (−2, 6) and (1, 9)

24. (4, 5) and (0, 5)

25. (1, 2) and (4, −3)

 ~

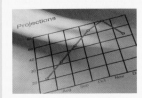

When linear equations are written in standard form (Ax + By = C), they can be graphed by finding the x- and y-intercepts and then drawing a line through those two points.
- In order to find the x-intercept, you must substitute 0 for y in the equation and then solve for x.
- In order to find the y-intercept, you must substitute 0 for x in the equation and then solve for y.

For example: Graph $2x - 3y = 6$ using the intercept method:

x-intercept	y-intercept
$2x - 3(0) = 6$	$2(0) - 3y = 6$
$2x = 6$	$-3y = 6$
$x = 3$	$y = -2$

Graph each of the following using the intercept method.

1. $5x + 4y = 20$

2. $-3x + y = 6$

3. $2x - 3y = 9$

4. $-3x + 5y = 15$

5. $4x - y = -8$

6. $4x + 7y = 14$

7. Convert each of the equations in **#1-6** into slope-intercept form using the method shown in Lesson 19. Use the slope-intercept equation to verify that each graph has the correct y-intercept and slope.

WRITING LINEAR EQUATIONS FOR GRAPHS

LESSON 17

 Write a linear equation for a given graph.

EXPLORE!   **FIND THE EQUATION**

Stacey and Mario like to go to the coffee shop before school. They decided to conduct an experiment to study the rate at which their coffees cool when left untouched on the table. The graph below shows the information they gathered.

Step 1: What is the real world meaning of the point (0, 160)? How about the point (10, 120)?

Step 2: Use the slope formula, $\frac{y_2 - y_1}{x_2 - x_1}$, to find the slope of the line. Does it matter which points from the graph you use in the formula?

Step 3: What is the real-world meaning of the slope?

Step 4: What is the y-intercept of this graph?

Step 5: Write an equation in slope-intercept form that represents this graph.

Step 6: Use your equation to determine the temperature of the coffee after 12 minutes.

Step 7: According to Stacey and Mario's experiment, the coffee continued to cool at the same rate every minute that passed. Do you think the coffee will continue to cool at this rate if the coffee is left on the table for one hour? Verify your theory using your equation.

A linear equation can be written for a specific line if you know the slope and y-intercept. The y-intercept can be determined by locating the point where the graph crosses the y-axis (0, b). The slope must be calculated using a slope triangle or the slope formula. Remember that when dealing with real-world graphs, the y-intercept is referred to as the start value and the slope is called the rate of change.

> **WRITING A LINEAR EQUATION FROM A GRAPH**
>
> 1. Locate the y-intercept on the graph.
> 2. Find the slope of the line.
> 3. Write the equation in slope-intercept form, $y = mx + b$.

EXAMPLE 1

Determine the slope and *y*-intercept of each graph. Write the equation for each graph in slope-intercept form.

a. 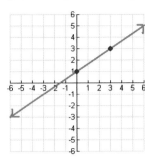   b. 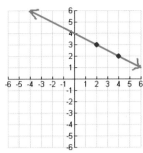   c.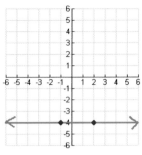

Solutions

a. The line crosses the *y*-axis at 1 so $b = 1$.
The slope triangle shows that $m = \frac{2}{3}$.
The equation in slope-intercept form is: $y = \frac{2}{3}x + 1$.

b. The line crosses the *y*-axis at 4 so $b = 4$.
The slope triangle shows that $m = -\frac{1}{2}$.
The equation in slope-intercept form is: $y = -\frac{1}{2}x + 4$.

c. The line crosses the *y*-axis at -4 so $b = -4$.
The slope triangle shows that $m = \frac{0}{3} = 0$.
The equation in slope-intercept form is $y = 0x - 4$ which can also be written as $y = -4$.

It is very useful to have equations for graphs that represent real-world situations because you can use the equation to predict future or past data.

EXAMPLE 2

Zach enjoys running each day after school. The graph below represents the distance Zach has traveled based on the number of minutes he has been running.

a. **Find the slope-intercept equation that represents the situation shown on the graph.**
b. **Use your equation to determine how far Zach will have gone in 28 minutes.**
c. **Use your equation to determine how long it will take Zach to run 10 miles.**

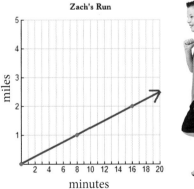

Solutions

a. The line crosses the *y*-axis at 0 so $b = 0$.
The two marked points are (8, 1) and (16, 2). Use the slope formula to calculate the slope.

$$\frac{y_2 - y_1}{x_2 - x_1} = \frac{2 - 1}{16 - 8} = \frac{1}{8}$$

The slope-intercept equation is $y = \frac{1}{8}x + 0$ or $y = \frac{1}{8}x$.

EXAMPLE 2
SOLUTIONS
(CONTINUED)

b. Since the *x*-values represent minutes, substitute 28 for *x* to determine how far Zach runs in 28 minutes:

$$y = \tfrac{1}{8}x$$
$$y = \tfrac{1}{8}(28)$$
$$y = \tfrac{28}{8} = 3\tfrac{4}{8} = 3\tfrac{1}{2} = 3.5$$

Zach runs 3.5 miles in 28 minutes.

c. Since the *y*-values represent miles, substitute 10 for *y* to determine how long it will take Zach to run 10 miles.

$$10 = \tfrac{1}{8}x$$
$$\tfrac{8}{1} \cdot 10 = \tfrac{1}{8}x \cdot \tfrac{8}{1}$$
$$80 = x$$

> Multiply by the reciprocal.

Zach's 10 mile run will take 80 minutes (one hour and twenty minutes).

Stacey and Mario found it was easy to write a slope-intercept equation from the graph because all they had to do was find the *y*-intercept and slope and put it into the form $y = mx + b$. They found the equation for their coffee experiment in the Explore! to be $y = -4x + 160$. They tested their formula by substituting values for the temperature of the coffee to see if it matched the number of minutes shown on the graph.

Temperature = 150°F → Since the *y*-values represent the temperature, substitute 150 for *y*.

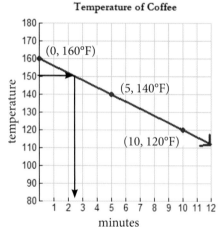

Temperature of Coffee

(0, 160°F)
(5, 140°F)
(10, 120°F)

$$\begin{array}{r|r} 150 = -4x + 160 \\ -160 \qquad\quad -160 \\ \hline -10 \;=\; -4x \\ \overline{-4} \quad \overline{-4} \\ 2.5 = x \end{array}$$

The coffee was 150° after 2.5 minutes.

Stacey and Mario used their formula to predict when their coffee would freeze.
Temperature = 32°F (freezing) → Since the *y*-values represent temperature, substitute 32 for *y*.

$$\begin{array}{r|r} 32 = -4x + 160 \\ -160 \qquad\quad -160 \\ \hline -128 \;=\; -4x \\ \overline{-4} \quad \overline{-4} \\ 32 = x \end{array}$$

According to the equation, the coffee would freeze in 32 minutes.

Stacey and Mario decided their formula only works for the first 10 minutes or so. It is not likely that coffee is going to reach a freezing temperature while it is sitting on the table.

EXERCISES

Identify the slope and *y*-intercept of each graph. Write the corresponding linear equation in slope-intercept form.

1.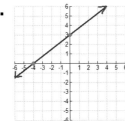

2.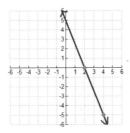

3.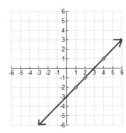

4.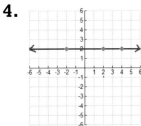

5.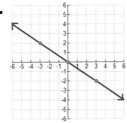

6.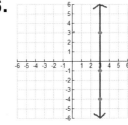

7. Skyler's total savings are shown on the graph.
   a. Find the slope-intercept equation that represents the graph.
   b. Use your equation to determine how much Skyler will have in his savings account after 18 months.
   c. Use your equation to determine how many months it will take before Skyler has $212 in his savings.

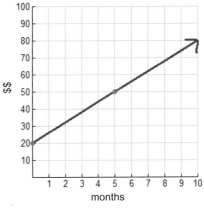

Skyler's Savings

8. Javier owns a car rental company. He provides the graph seen at left for his customers to see the price for renting a sedan based on the number of miles they drive.
   a. Find the equation (in slope-intercept form) that represents the amount Javier charges based on the number of miles driven.
   b. Determine the amount a customer will have to pay if she rents a sedan and drives it 120 miles.
   c. Leticia rented a sedan from Javier. When she returned it, her bill was $38.50. How many miles did she drive?

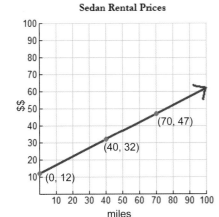

Sedan Rental Prices

(70, 47)

(40, 32)

(0, 12)

miles

9. At two different times during the summer, Kirsten measured the height of a sunflower she had planted in May. She measured it when she first planted the flower and then again 3 weeks later.

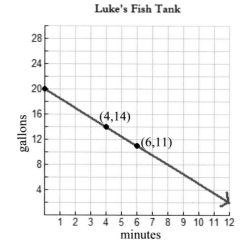

Kirsten's Sunflower

    a. Find the slope-intercept equation that represents the height of Kirsten's flower based on the number of weeks since she planted it.

    b. Use your equation to determine exactly how tall the sunflower will be after 8 weeks.

    c. Use your equation to determine how many weeks have passed if the plant is 47 inches tall.

10. Luke drained his 20-gallon fish tank. At two different times, he measured the amount of water left in the tank. He graphed the information on the graph shown at right.

    a. Find the slope-intercept equation that represents the number of gallons left in the fish tank since he began draining it.

    b. Use your equation to determine how much water will be left in the tank after 10 minutes.

    c. When will the water be completely drained from the tank?

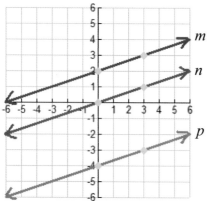

11. Use the graph at left to answer the following questions.

    a. Find the slope-intercept equations for lines m, n and p.

    b. What do the three equations have in common?

    c. What geometry term can be used to describe the relationship between these three lines?

12. Evaluate the following expressions when $x = 3$ and $y = -4$

    a. $2x + 5y$ **b.** $-4x - 6y$ **c.** $\frac{1}{2}y - 5x$

State whether each equation is true or false for the values of the variables given.

13. $y = 3x + 1$ when $x = 2$ and $y = 6$ **14.** $y = \frac{4}{3}x - 4$ when $x = 6$ and $y = 4$

15. $y = -2x + 7$ when $x = 5$ and $y = -3$ **16.** $y = \frac{1}{4}x$ when $x = 10$ and $y = 2$

17. $y = 4 - x$ when $x = 3$ and $y = 1$ **18.** $y = 2 - \frac{1}{2}x$ when $x = 1$ and $y = 2$

TIC-TAC-TOE ~ GRAPHING DESIGN

Lines are used in many types of artwork. Use a large sheet of graph paper to create a piece of artwork.

Step 1: Draw a coordinate plane that includes all four quadrants.

Step 2: Create a design using at least 15 different lines. Make sure over two-thirds of the lines are not vertical or horizontal.

Step 3: Write the equations for each line on the back of your piece of artwork.

Step 4: Color your artwork and sign the bottom right corner.

TIC-TAC-TOE ~ PARALLEL OR PERPENDICULAR LINES

Perpendicular lines are lines that intersect at a 90° angle. Parallel lines never intersect. Each pair of lines given below is either parallel or perpendicular.

SET #1	SET #2	SET #3	SET #4	SET #5
$y = 2x + 3$	$-3x + 2y = 6$	$y - x = 5$	$-x + 2y = -4$	$y = \frac{1}{3}x + 3$
$y = 2x - 4$	$y = -\frac{2}{3}x - 4$	$y = x - 2$	$4x + 2y = 8$	$y = -3x - 1$

Step 1: If necessary, convert each equation into slope-intercept form using the method shown in Lesson 19.

Step 2: Graph each pair of equations on the same coordinate plane.

Step 3: State whether each pair of lines is parallel or perpendicular.

Step 4: After completing all five sets of graphs, develop a hypothesis on how to use the slope-intercept equation to determine if lines are parallel or perpendicular without graphing. Explain how you arrived at your hypothesis.

WRITING LINEAR EQUATIONS FROM KEY INFORMATION

LESSON 18

 Write a linear equation in slope-intercept form when given information about the line.

There are two pieces of information you need to be able to write an equation in slope-intercept form: the slope and the *y*-intercept. You learned how to determine the equation when given a graph of the linear equation. In this lesson you will find equations for specific lines when given different pieces of information about the lines.

When you are given the slope and the *y*-intercept for a line you need to insert the information into $y = mx + b$ for the appropriate variables.

EXAMPLE 1	**Write the equation of a line that has a slope of −2 and *y*-intercept of 5.**
SOLUTION	Write the general slope-intercept equation. $\qquad y = mx + b$
	Substitute −2 for *m* since *m* represents the slope. $\qquad y = -2x + b$
	Substitute 5 for *b* since *b* represents the *y*-intercept. $\qquad y = -2x + 5$
	The equation is $y = -2x + 5$.

When you are not directly given the slope and *y*-intercept, there are steps you can follow to find both the slope and *y*-intercept. Once you have both the slope and *y*-intercept, you can write a linear equation in slope-intercept form.

WRITING A LINEAR EQUATION WHEN GIVEN KEY INFORMATION

1. Find the slope (*m*) of the line.
2. Find the *y*-intercept (*b*) of the line. If necessary, substitute the slope for *m* and one ordered pair (*x*, *y*) for the corresponding variables in the equation $y = mx + b$. Solve for *b*.
3. Write the equation in the form $y = mx + b$.

EXAMPLE 2	**Write the equation of a line that has a slope of $\frac{4}{3}$ and goes through the point $(-3, 1)$.**

SOLUTION

The slope is given.
$$m = \frac{4}{3}$$

Write the slope-intercept equation with the slope.
$$y = \frac{4}{3}x + b$$

Find the y-intercept, b, by substituting the given point $(-3, 1)$ for x and y in the slope-intercept equation.
$$1 = \frac{4}{3}(-3) + b$$
$$1 = -4 + b$$

Solve for b.
$$\frac{+4 \quad\quad +4}{5 = b}$$

Write the equation by substituting m and b.
$$y = \frac{4}{3}x + 5$$

Check by graphing.

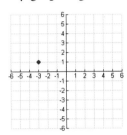 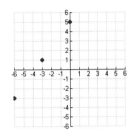 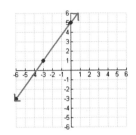

Plot the point $(-3, 1)$. at least two more points.   Use the slope $\frac{4}{3}$ to find the points.   Draw a line through

If you are given two points on a line, first find the slope using the slope formula or a slope triangle. Then follow the process in Example 2 to write the slope-intercept equation.

EXPLORE!

TRIANGLE LINES

A triangle consists of three line segments. A segment is a portion of a line.

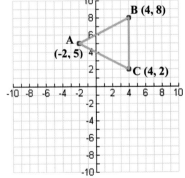

Step 1: Find the equation of the line that contains $\overline{AB}$.

Step 2: Find the equation of the line that contains $\overline{AC}$.

Step 3: Find the equation of the line that contains $\overline{BC}$.

Step 4: Ryan made his own triangle. He chose three points and wants you to find the equations of the three lines that make up his triangle. His points are $(3, 3)$, $(-2, -7)$ and $(-7, -2)$. Can you find the three linear equations that intersect to make his triangle?

Step 5: The points where the line segments meet in a triangle are called the vertices. Graph your three lines on a piece of graph paper using the slope and y-intercepts from your equations. Does the triangle that is formed have the same three vertices that Ryan chose?

EXERCISES

Write an equation in slope-intercept form when given the slope and *y*-intercept.

1. slope = $\frac{6}{5}$, *y*-intercept = 8

2. slope = −4, *y*-intercept = 1

3. slope = 1, *y*-intercept = 2

4. slope = 0, *y*-intercept = −3

5. In 2000, the population of Oregon was approximately 3,400,000 people. During the next six years, the population increased by approximately 50,000 people each year.

   a. Write an equation in slope-intercept form that represents the population, *y*, of Oregon in terms of the number of years, *x*, since 2000.
   b. Estimate the population of Oregon in 2020 if this trend continues.

Write an equation in slope-intercept form when given the slope and one point on the line.

6. slope = 2, goes through the point (1, −4)

7. slope = $-\frac{3}{4}$, goes through the point (4, 2)

8. slope = −1, goes through the point (−2, 3)

9. slope = $\frac{5}{2}$, goes through the point (−6, −10)

10. slope = $\frac{1}{2}$, goes through the point (3, 4)

11. slope = 0, goes through the point (11, 8)

12. One Portland taxi company charges an initial fee plus $0.10 for each minute of the ride. Tammy was in the taxi for 14 minutes. The cost was $5.40. Let *x* represent the number of minutes and *y* represent the total cost of the taxi ride.
   a. Identify the slope and one ordered pair from the information given.
   b. Find the equation of the line that fits this information.
   c. Joe uses this taxi company for a 30 minute ride. How much should he expect to pay?

Write an equation in slope-intercept form when given two points.

13. goes through the points (1, 2) and (3, 8)

14. goes through the points (−5, 9) and (4, 0)

15. goes through the points (6, 9) and (−3, 6)

16. goes through the points (8, −4) and (−2, 1)

17. goes through the points (10, 6) and (0, −2)

18. goes through the points (4, −5) and (1, −2)

19. goes through the points (7, 3) and (0, 3)

20. goes through the points (1, −5) and (1, 4)

21. At 2 weeks old, Bob's baby sister weighed 9 pounds. When she was 8 weeks old, she weighed 12 pounds. Let x represent how old the baby is in weeks and y represent the baby's weight in pounds.

    a. Write two ordered pairs that use the data about Bob's sister.

    b. Find the equation of the line that goes through these two points.

    c. If Bob's sister continues to grow at this rate, how much will she weigh when she is 20 weeks old? Is this reasonable? Why or why not?

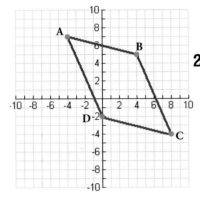

22. Four line segments make the four sides of a quadrilateral on the coordinate plane to the left. Find the equations of the lines containing each side: $\overline{AB}$, $\overline{BC}$, $\overline{CD}$, $\overline{AD}$. Are there any similarities in the equations for lines $\overline{AB}$ and $\overline{CD}$? How about $\overline{BC}$ and $\overline{AD}$?

23. A raft rental company on the Deschutes River rents rafts for a set fee plus an additional charge per hour. Francis asked two different people how many hours they had rented their rafts for and how much it cost. One rented a raft for 6 hours and paid $32. Another rented a raft for 11 hours and paid $47. Let x represent the length of time in hours and let y represent the total cost.

    a. Write two ordered pairs that use the data Francis collected.

    b. Find the equation of the line that goes through these two points.

    c. What number in the linear equation represents the amount of the set fee?

    d. What is the real world meaning of the slope in this equation?

    e. How much will someone pay for a raft rental from this company if he only keeps the raft for 4 hours?

REVIEW

Write the linear equation for each graph in slope-intercept form.

24.

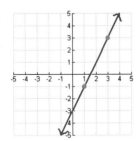

25.

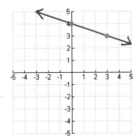

26.

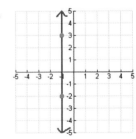

Draw a coordinate plane for each problem. Graph each equation. Clearly mark three points on the line.

27. $y = \frac{5}{3}x - 4$

28. $y = -4x + 5$

29. $x = 3$

Write the slope-intercept equation that matches the data.

30.

Hours	Distance Traveled
0	45
1	75
2	105
3	135
4	165

31.

Days	Plant Height
1	3.3
2	3.6
6	4.8
8	5.4
10	6.0

32.

Cups of Coffee Sold	Profit $
0	−15
4	−7
9	3
15	15
100	185

TIC-TAC-TOE ~ LINES OF BEST FIT

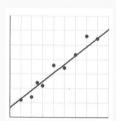

You have learned how to take real-world data and graph the data points on a scatter plot. When real-world data is collected there is usually not a single line that passes through all of the data points, but you can often see a linear pattern on the scatter plot. In this activity, you will find a line that best fits the data you are given. This line is called the line of best fit. The steps to finding a line of best fit are shown in the box below.

FINDING A LINE OF BEST FIT

1. Plot the data points and determine the general direction of the data.
2. Draw a line in that general direction that has approximately the same number of points above and below the line.
3. Locate two points on your line. Approximate the *x*- and *y*-coordinates for each point (these do not need to be data points from the original data).
4. Find the slope-intercept equation of the line.

The data in the table shows the fare costs for different lengths of rides on the city bus.

1. Graph the data points.

2. Draw a line of best fit.

3. Find the equation for the line of best fit.

4. Use your equation to predict the cost to ride this city bus 50 miles.

5. Use your equation to predict how far you could ride the bus for $10.

Miles	Cost
2	$1.00
5	$1.75
10	$2.00
12	$2.50
16	$2.50
20	$3.25
26	$3.50
30	$4.75

DIFFERENT FORMS OF LINEAR EQUATIONS

 Convert different forms of linear equations to slope-intercept form.

Linear equations come in many different forms. So far in this book, you have used the slope-intercept form. The slope-intercept form gives both the slope and y-intercept of the graph. In this lesson, you will work with linear equations in other forms and convert them into slope-intercept form in order to graph the equations.

STANDARD FORM: $Ax + By = C$ where A and B are not both zero.
POINT-SLOPE FORM: $y - y_1 = m(x - x_1)$ or $y = m(x - x_1) + y_1$

It is important to know how to change equations into forms you can recognize and use. The key to converting a linear equation into slope-intercept form is to remove all parentheses using the Distributive Property and then isolating the y-variable.

Converting STANDARD FORM to SLOPE-INTERCEPT FORM

Process	Example: $-3x + 4y = 12$
Step 1: Move the term containing the x-value to the other side of the = sign with the constant.	$\begin{array}{r} -3x + 4y = 12 \\ +3x \qquad\qquad +3x \end{array}$
Step 2: Re-write the equation. Remember that you cannot combine terms unless they are like terms.	$4y = 12 + 3x$
Step 3: Isolate y by dividing by the coefficient on the y-value. Divide EVERY TERM by the coefficient of y.	$\dfrac{4y}{4} = \dfrac{12 + 3x}{4}$
Step 4: Re-write the equation. Leave the coefficient of x as a simplified fraction when you divide because this is the slope of the graph.	$y = 3 + \frac{3}{4}x$ or $y = \frac{3}{4}x + 3$

EXAMPLE 1

Convert the following from STANDARD form to SLOPE-INTERCEPT form.
a. $-5x + 2y = -20$ b. $x - 3y = 9$

> Don't forget there is a 1 in front of the x.

SOLUTIONS

a. $\begin{array}{r} -5x + 2y = -20 \\ +5x \qquad\qquad +5x \end{array}$

$\dfrac{2y}{2} = \dfrac{-20 + 5x}{2}$

$y = -10 + \frac{5}{2}x$
or
$y = \frac{5}{2}x - 10$

b. $\begin{array}{r} x - 3y = 9 \\ -x \qquad\quad -x \end{array}$

$\dfrac{-3y}{-3} = \dfrac{9 - x}{-3}$

$y = -3 + \frac{1}{3}x$
or
$y = \frac{1}{3}x - 3$

Converting POINT-SLOPE FORM to SLOPE-INTERCEPT FORM

Process	Example: $y - 5 = 2(x + 1)$
Step 1: Use the Distributive Property to remove any parentheses (**Lesson 3**).	$y - 5 = 2(x + 1) \rightarrow y - 5 = 2x + 2$
Step 2: Combine like terms that are on the same side of the equals sign.	*Not necessary in this example.*
Step 3: Get y "by itself" by balancing the equation using the Properties of Equality (**Lesson 4**).	$\begin{array}{r} y - 5 = 2x + 2 \\ +5 \quad\quad +5 \end{array}$
Step 4: Write final answer in form $y = mx + b$.	$y = 2x + 7$

EXAMPLE 2

Convert the following from POINT-SLOPE form to SLOPE-INTERCEPT form.

a. $y = \frac{1}{2}(x - 4) + 1$ 　　　　　　b. $y + 4 = -3(x - 2)$

SOLUTIONS

A. $y = \frac{1}{2}(x - 4) + 1$

$y = \frac{1}{2}x - 2 + 1$

$y = \frac{1}{2}x - 1$

> Combine like terms.

b. $y + 4 = -3(x - 2)$

$y + 4 = -3x + 6$

$\quad\; -4 \quad\quad\;\; -4$

$y = -3x + 2$

> Balance the equation.

In **Example 2**, the equation $y = \frac{1}{2}(x - 4) + 1$ is **equivalent** to $y = \frac{1}{2}x - 1$. That means that both equations represent the same line even though the equations look different. Linear equations can come in many forms, but every linear equation can be converted to an equivalent slope-intercept equation. Try the Explore! to practice converting all types of equations to slope-intercept form.

CONVERTING EQUATIONS TO SLOPE-INTERCEPT FORM

1. Use the Distributive Property to remove any parentheses.
2. Combine all like terms on the same side of the equals sign.
3. Isolate y by balancing the equation using the Properties of Equality.
4. Re-write the equation in slope-intercept form.

EXPLORE!　　　　　　　　　　　　　　　　　　　**ONE OF THESE THINGS**

In each set of four equations "one of these things is not like the other". Three of the linear equations in each set are equivalent and one is not. For each set, find the three that are similar and give the slope-intercept form that they are equivalent to. Graph that equation on a coordinate plane.

SET 1

$y + 10 = 3(x + 2)$
$y = 1 + 3(x + 1)$
$-9x + 3y = -12$
$6x - 2y = 8$

SET 2

$2x + 4y = 4$
$y = \frac{1}{2}(x + 6) + 4$
$y + 1 = -\frac{1}{2}(x - 4)$
$5x + 10y = 10$

EXERCISES

Match each equation to its equivalent equation in slope-intercept form.

1. $y + 6 = 3(x + 2)$

2. $y = \frac{1}{2}(x + 8) - 2$

3. $y + 1 = 1(x - 3)$

4. $-4x + y = -2$

5. $2x - 4y = -4$

6. $2x + 4y = 8$

A. $y = 4x - 2$

B. $y = \frac{1}{2}x + 2$

C. $y = 3x$

D. $y = -\frac{1}{2}x + 2$

E. $y = x - 4$

F. $y = \frac{1}{2}x + 1$

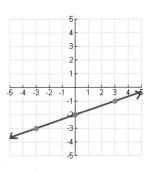

Convert each equation to slope-intercept form.

7. $y + 3 = 4(x + 6)$

8. $6x + 2y = 12$

9. $y = -2 + \frac{1}{3}(x + 9)$

10. $2x - 5y = -15$

11. $-x - 2y = 2$

12. $y - 1 = -2(x - 5)$

13. $y = \frac{3}{4}(x + 12) - 2$

14. $-7x + y = 6$

15. $y + 15 = 4(x + 6)$

One of the two equations listed in each problem matches the graph. Determine which equation is represented by the graph.

16. $y - 1 = 2(x + 1)$
OR
$6x + 3y = 9$

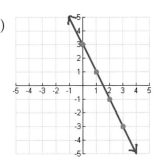

17. $6x + 2y = -4$
OR
$y = \frac{1}{3}(x - 9) + 1$

REVIEW

Write an equation in slope-intercept form that satisfies the information given about the line.

18. has a slope of $\frac{5}{2}$ and a y-intercept of 3

19. has a slope of -3 and goes through the point $(3, 1)$

20. has a slope of 5 and goes through the origin

21. goes through the points $(6, 1)$ and $(10, -1)$

22. goes through the points $(-2, 5)$ and $(4, 11)$

23. has a slope of 0 and a y-intercept of -5

24. goes through the points $(4, 1)$ and $(4, 9)$

25. goes through the points $(1, -3)$ and $(2, -6)$

TIC-TAC-TOE ~ EQUIVALENT EQUATIONS

Step 1: On a sheet of notebook paper, write 10 linear equations in point-slope or standard form. Next to each equation, write the equivalent linear equation in slope-intercept form.

Step 2: Take a blank sheet of white paper and fold it down the middle vertically. Cut the front sheet into equal-sized sections.

Step 3: Write a linear equation from your list that is not in slope-intercept form on each flap. Inside the flap, show the steps to reach the equivalent equation that is in slope-intercept form.

TIC-TAC-TOE ~ CLASS COMPETITION

Create a game that can be played with the whole class as a review for the material in this Block. Create a "Teacher's Guide" with the four categories shown below. In each category, generate three questions that vary in level of difficulty from easiest to hardest. Include the answer for each question in the "Teacher's Guide".

Writing Equations from Graphs	Writing Equations from Key Information	Graphing Linear Equations	Equivalent Equations
Level 1	Level 1	Level 1	Level 1
Level 2	Level 2	Level 2	Level 2
Level 3	Level 3	Level 3	Level 3

Create a document explaining the class competition rules. Here are some things to consider:

- How many teams should there be?
- How are the teams decided?
- How do the teams answer the questions (as individuals or as a team)?
- How much time does a team have to answer a question?
- What happens if a team gets the answer wrong?
- How do teams score points?
- When is the game over?

MORE GRAPHING LINEAR EQUATIONS

LESSON 20

 Graph linear equations that are not written in slope-intercept form.

EXPLORE!   **MATCH ME**

Jared and Wendy are playing a matching game. Each card in the deck has either a graph or a linear equation on it. The goal of the game is to be the first to match the six Equation Cards to their corresponding Graph Cards.

Step 1: Convert each Equation Card to slope-intercept form.

Step 2: Match each Equation Card to its corresponding Graph Card.

1 $y + 6 = -2(x - 5)$

A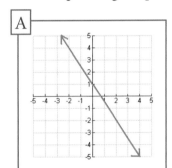

2 $6y = -12$

B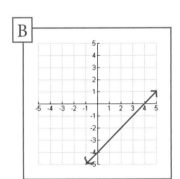

C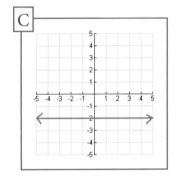

3 $y = -\frac{1}{3}(x + 3) + 1$

4 $y - 5 = 2(x - 4)$

D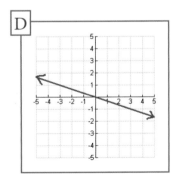

5 $3x + 2y = 2$

E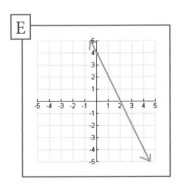

6 $-3x + 3y = -12$

F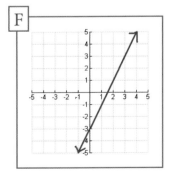

Step 3: On your own paper, create two more Equation Cards and their corresponding graph cards that could be used in a future matching game.

No matter what form a linear equation is written in, it can be converted to slope-intercept form and graphed. Remember that the key steps to converting an equation into slope-intercept form include using the Distributive Property and isolating the *y*-variable.

EXAMPLE 1

Convert the following equations to slope-intercept form and then graph.
a. $4x + 3y = 12$ **b.** $y = \frac{1}{2}(x - 4) + 3$

SOLUTIONS

A. $4x + 3y = 12$

$\underline{-4x \qquad\qquad -4x}$

$\dfrac{3y}{3} = \dfrac{12 - 4x}{3}$

$y = 4 - \frac{4}{3}x$

b. $y = \frac{1}{2}(x - 4) + 3$

$y = \frac{1}{2}x - 2 + 3$

$y = \frac{1}{2}x + 1$

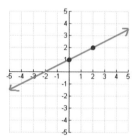

Every line has an infinite number of points that make up the line. In certain situations, verification is needed to determine whether or not a point lies on a certain line. In order to determine this, the equation DOES NOT need to be graphed. The *x*- and *y*-values from the ordered pair can be substituted for the *x*-and *y*-variables in the linear equation. If the values make the equation true, then the point lies on the line.

EXAMPLE 2

Determine if each point is on the given line.
a. Is the point (3, −4) on the line $5x + 2y = 7$?
b. Is the point (0, 5) on the line $y + 3 = 2(x + 3)$?

SOLUTIONS

a. Substitute 3 for *x* and −4 for *y*.

$5x + 2y = 7$
$5(3) + 2(-4) \overset{?}{=} 7$
$15 + -8 \overset{?}{=} 7$
$7 = 7$

> The point is on this line.

b. Substitute 0 for *x* and 5 for *y*.

$y + 3 = 2(x + 3)$
$5 + 3 \overset{?}{=} 2(0 + 3)$
$8 \overset{?}{=} 2(3)$
$8 \neq 6$

> The point is NOT on this line.

EXERCISES

Convert each equation to slope-intercept form and graph. Clearly mark at least three points on each line.

1. $-5x + 2y = -8$

2. $y - 8 = -3(x + 1)$

3. $y = 1 + \frac{1}{2}(x + 4)$

4. $x + 4y = 12$

5. $4x - 3y = 6$

6. $y = 2(x + 5) - 8$

7. $4x = 8$

8. $y = \frac{3}{4}(x + 8) - 9$

9. $y + 6 = 3(x + 2)$

10. $y - 11 = -\frac{5}{2}(x + 2)$

11. $-x + y = -6$

12. $-5y = 20$

13. Write a linear equation that is not in slope-intercept form. Convert it to slope-intercept form and graph it.

14. Patti signed up for a cell phone plan that charges an initial monthly fee and a set rate per minute she talks on the phone each month. The equation she was given to calculate her total bill, y, was $y = 0.1(x + 20) + 7$ where x represents the number of minutes she talks on the phone in one month.
   a. Convert the equation into slope-intercept form.
   b. What is Patti's initial fee each month?
   c. What is her rate per minute?
   d. Last month, Patti talked on the phone 427 minutes. How much will her total bill be for last month?

15. Is the point $(-1, 4)$ on the line $3x + 2y = 5$?

16. Is the point $(6, 0)$ on the line $y = -11 + 2(x - 1)$?

17. Is the point $(0, 0)$ on the line $y = -\frac{1}{2}(x + 4) + 2$?

18. Is the point $(2, 10)$ on the line $5x - y = 0$?

19. Is the point $(-6, -2)$ on the line $-x + 2y = -10$?

20. Is the point $(-\frac{1}{2}, 3)$ on the line $y = 2 - 2x$?

21. Vicky decided to buy tickets to the local Razorbacks baseball games. She learned she must first become a Razorback Club member for $14 and then pay $2.50 per ticket to attend the games. The equation that represents the total cost, C, based on the number of games, g, she attends is $C = 14 + 2.50g$. Vicky purchased 12 games plus the membership fee. The ticket sales person charged her $34. Was she charged correctly? If not, how much should she have been charged?

In each set of three linear equations, two are equivalent. Identify the one linear equation that is not equivalent to the others in the set.

22. $\begin{cases} 2x + 4y = 8 \\ y = \frac{1}{2}x - 2 \\ y = -\frac{1}{2}x + 2 \end{cases}$

23. $\begin{cases} y = 3x - 4 \\ y = 3(x - 2) + 2 \\ -3x + y = 4 \end{cases}$

24. $\begin{cases} y = x - 1 \\ 5x + 5y = -5 \\ y = -(x + 6) + 5 \end{cases}$

REVIEW

Write an equation in slope-intercept form that is represented by the given information.

25.

x	y
0	6
1	4
2	2
3	0

26. has a slope of −2 and y-intercept of 1

27.
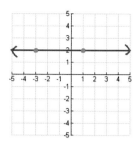

28. goes through the points (−3, 3) and (2, 8)

29.
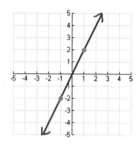

30.

x	y
1	−1
3	9
6	24
8	34

31.

32.

x	y
4	−1
4	3
4	5
4	7

33. has a slope of $\frac{1}{3}$ and goes through the point (6, 1)

TIC-TAC-TOE ~ CAREERS USING ALGEBRA

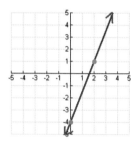

Linear equations are an essential part of Algebra I. There are many career choices where knowledge of algebra is crucial. Research at least two different careers that require the use of algebra. Write a 1-2 page report about these careers.

Include the following in your report for each career:
- Description of the career
- How the career includes the use of algebra
- How much schooling is required for the career

TIC-TAC-TOE ~ EXPONENTIAL EQUATIONS

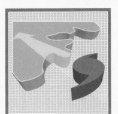

Exponential equations are used to predict growth and decay. Exponential equations have a start value and multiplication as the repeated operation. The start value is represented by the variable b and the constant multiplier is represented by the variable m in the equation $y = b \cdot m^x$.

Most growth and decay situations involve percentages. For example, a car may depreciate (decrease in value) at a rate of 12% per year. Or the number of bacteria might increase by 40% each day. In order to find the value of m with percentages, you must first start with 100% and then add or subtract the given percentage depending on whether it is increasing or decreasing in value. The percent must be converted to a decimal.

Car depreciating by 12% = 100% − 12% = 88% = 0.88
Bacteria increasing by 40% = 100% + 40% = 140% = 1.40

> Numbers to be used as m in the equation.

A car was purchased for $14,000 and depreciates at a rate of 12% per year. This means it keeps 88% of its value. The exponential equation would be:
$$y = 14{,}000 \cdot 0.88^x$$

You can find the new value of the car after any number of years by substituting the number of years for x. For example, to find the value of the car after 5 years, substitute 5 for x. Remember to follow the order of operations when calculating.
$$y = 14{,}000 \cdot 0.88^5 \approx \$7{,}388.25$$

Answer each of the following exercises using the exponential equation $y = b \cdot m^x$.

1. Mary bought a brand new car in 2004 for $22,000. She was told that her model of car has an annual depreciation rate of 11%.
  a. How much was Mary's car worth if she sold it in 2007?
  b. How much will her car be worth if she waits and sells it in 2015?

2. Imar made $4,000 over the summer and wants to invest it for the future. He finds a bank that offers him 6% growth each year.
  a. How much will Imar have in the account after 3 years?
  b. How much will he have after 8 years?
  c. After approximately how many years will he have doubled his money?

3. The number of bacteria in a kitchen sink increases by 60% each day the sink remains uncleaned. The sink currently has 15 bacteria.
  a. How many bacteria will be present after 10 days of not washing the sink?
  b. Approximately how long will it take before there are at least 1,000 bacteria in the sink?

4. Write two of your own growth or decay application problems and find the solutions.

INTRODUCTION TO NON - LINEAR FUNCTIONS

LESSON 21

 Recognize linear, quadratic, exponential and inverse variation functions.

In this textbook you have learned how to graph linear functions when written in different forms. However, not all functions produce a linear graph. In this lesson you will learn about a few types of non-linear functions. Non-linear functions are functions that, when graphed, do not form a line. There are a large variety of non-linear functions, many of which you will learn about in higher-level mathematics.

In a linear function, each equal "step" that the x-value increases, the y-value increases or decreases a consistent amount.

$y = 4x + 5$

x	y	
0	5	+4
1	9	+4
2	13	+4
3	17	
4	21	

In a non-linear function, there is not a consistent adding or subtracting pattern for each equal "step", although each type of non-linear function does have a unique pattern. In this lesson you will examine quadratic functions, exponential functions and inverse variation functions. Each type of non-linear function has a parent graph. The parent graphs are the most basic graph of each non-linear function.

EXPLORE!   NON-LINEAR CURVES

The Quadratic Function

Step 1: The parent graph of the quadratic function is the graph of $y = x^2$. Copy the table at right on your own paper and fill in the missing values.

Step 2: Plot the (x, y) points from the table. Connect the points with a curved line. Describe what the graph looks like.

$y = x^2$

x	y
−3	$(-3)^2 = 9$
−2	$(-2)^2 = 4$
−1	
0	
1	
2	
3	

The Exponential Function

Step 3: One parent graph of an exponential function is the graph of $y = 2^x$. Copy the table at right on your own paper and fill in the missing values using a calculator.

Step 4: Plot the (x, y) points from the table. Connect the points with a curved line. Describe what the graph looks like.

$y = 2^x$

x	y
−3	$2^{(-3)} = 0.125$
−2	$2^{(-2)} = 0.25$
−1	$2^{(-1)} = 0.5$
0	
1	
2	
3	

The parent graphs of three non-linear functions are shown below. Other graphs in each "family" have the same shape as the parent graph but may be stretched, shrunk, moved or flipped.

Quadratic Functions

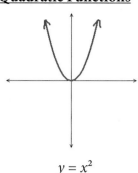

$$y = x^2$$

Exponential Functions

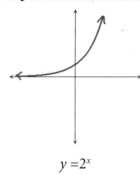

$$y = 2^x$$

Inverse Variation Functions

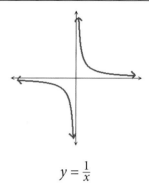

$$y = \frac{1}{x}$$

EXAMPLE 1

Determine if each graph, table or equation is linear or non-linear. If it is non-linear, identify the type of function (quadratic, exponential or inverse variation).

a. $y = 3x - 2$

b.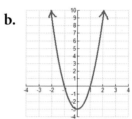

c.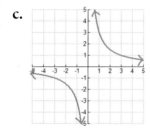

d.

x	y
-1	$\frac{1}{3}$
0	1
1	3
2	9
3	27

SOLUTIONS

a. LINEAR. This equation is linear because it is in slope-intercept form.

b. NON-LINEAR. This graph forms a "U" shape so it is a quadratic function.

c. NON-LINEAR. The graph matches the inverse variation parent graph.

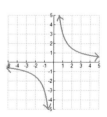

d. NON-LINEAR. Graph the data points to see that it matches the parent function graph of the exponential function.

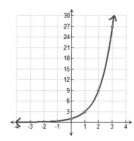

Non-linear equations are used in the real world. Banks use exponential functions to calculate interest. Architects use quadratic functions when designing bridges. Businessmen use quadratic functions to determine costs of products in order to maximize profits. Chemists use exponential functions to calculate the rate of bacteria growth. An example of a real-world use of the inverse variation function is found in the creation of levers.

EXERCISES

 Copy each table and use the given equation to fill in the missing values.

1. $y = x^2 + 2$

x	y
−2	$(-2)^2 + 2 = 6$
−1	
0	
1	
2	

2. $y = 3^x$

x	y
−2	$3^{(-2)} = \frac{1}{9}$
−1	
0	
1	
2	

3. $y = 2x - 5$

x	y
−2	$2(-2) - 5 = -9$
−1	
0	
1	
2	

4. Graph the five points from the table in **Exercise 1** on a coordinate plane. What type of non-linear equation is this?

5. Graph the five points from the table in **Exercise 2** on a coordinate plane. What type of non-linear equation is this?

6. Graph the five points from the table in **Exercise 3** on a coordinate plane. What type of equation is this?

Determine if each graph, table or equation is linear or non-linear. If it is non-linear, identify the type of graph (quadratic, exponential or inverse variation).

7.

x	y
−2	$\frac{1}{16}$
−1	$\frac{1}{4}$
0	1
1	4
2	16

8. $y = (x + 1)^2$

9.

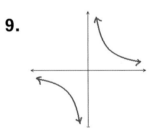

10.

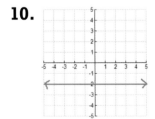

11.

x	y
−2	−2
−1	1
0	4
1	7
2	10

12. $y = 4^x$

13. A bacteria culture begins with 5 cells and doubles every hour. This situation can be represented by the exponential function $y = 5 \cdot 2^x$ where x represents the number of hours and y represents the number of bacteria. How many bacteria will be in the culture after 7 hours?

14. The path of a ball thrown through the air can be modeled by the equation $y = -4.9x^2 + 17x + 3.4$ when x is the time in seconds and y is the height of the ball in meters. Find the height of the ball after 3 seconds.

REVIEW

Solve each equation. Check your solution.

15. $x - 24 = 72$

16. $\frac{x}{5} = -11$

17. $8x + 13 = 61$

18. $17 = -4x + 2$

19. $2x + 7 = 5x - 8$

20. $3(x - 5) = -9$

Draw a coordinate plane for each problem and graph the given equation. Clearly mark three points on the line.

21. $y = \frac{1}{3}x - 3$

22. $y = 1$

23. $y = 2x + 1$

24. $y = x$

25. $y = -\frac{5}{2}x + 4$

26. $y = -4x + 9$

27. $x = -1$

28. $y = -\frac{1}{2}(x - 6) - 1$

29. $2x + 5y = 10$

Quadratic functions can be described as being "U" shaped. Linear equations can be easily graphed when in slope-intercept form. Similarly, quadratic functions can be easily graphed when in factored form: $y = (x - a)(x - b)$. You need to know the two x-intercepts and the vertex (maximum or minimum point on the graph) in order to graph a simple quadratic function.

For example: Graph $y = (x - 4)(x + 2)$.

Step 1: Locate the x-intercepts. The x-intercepts can be found by setting the expressions inside each parentheses equal to 0 and solving.

$$x - 4 = 0 \qquad\qquad x + 2 = 0$$
$$\underline{+4 \;\;|\; +4} \qquad\qquad \underline{-2 \;\;|\; -2}$$
$$x = 4 \qquad\qquad\qquad x = -2$$

Step 2: Average the x-intercepts by adding them together and then dividing the sum by 2. This is the x-coordinate of the vertex.

$$\frac{4 + -2}{2} = 1$$

Step 3: Substitute the number from **Step 2** back into the original equation to find the y-coordinate of the vertex.
$$y = (1 - 4)(1 + 2)$$
$$y = (-3)(3) = -9$$

Step 4: Graph the quadratic function. Connect the three points with a smooth curve.

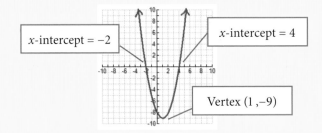

x-intercept = −2

x-intercept = 4

Vertex (1 ,−9)

Graph the following quadratic functions following the four steps shown above.

1. $y = (x - 2)(x - 6)$ **2.** $y = (x - 5)(x + 1)$

3. $y = (x - 2)(x + 2)$ **4.** $y = (x + 5)(x + 1)$

Vocabulary

continuous	equivalent	parent graph
discrete	non-linear functions	slope-intercept form

Graph linear equations in slope-intercept form.
Write a linear equation for a given graph.
Write a linear equation in slope-intercept form when given information about the line.
Convert different forms of linear equations to slope-intercept form.
Graph linear equations that are not written in slope-intercept form.
Recognize linear, quadratic, exponential and inverse variation functions.

Lesson 16 ~ Graphing Using Slope-Intercept Form

• •

Draw a coordinate plane for each problem and graph the given equation. Clearly mark three points on the line.

1. $y = 3x - 4$ **2.** $y = \frac{2}{3}x + 3$ **3.** $y = x - 1$

4. $y = -2x$ **5.** $x = 3$ **6.** $y = 6 + \frac{4}{3}x$

7. Create a linear equation that satisfies each condition. Graph your equations on a coordinate plane.
     a. Slope = 2 and a negative y-intercept
     b. Slope = 0 and a y-intercept of -3
     c. A negative slope and a positive y-intercept
     d. A positive slope and a y-intercept of 0

Lesson 17 ~ Writing Linear Equations for Graphs

• •

Identify the slope and y-intercept of each graph and write the corresponding linear equation in slope-intercept form.

8.
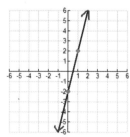

9.
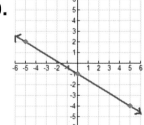

10.
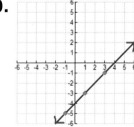

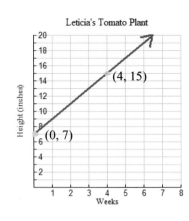

Leticia's Tomato Plant

(4, 15)

(0, 7)

Height (inches)

Weeks

11. At two different times during the summer, Leticia measured the height of a tomato plant she had planted in June. She measured it when she first planted it and then again 4 weeks later.

    a. Find the slope-intercept equation that represents the height of Leticia's tomato plant based on the number of weeks since she planted it.

    b. Use your equation to determine exactly how tall the tomato plant will be after 7 weeks.

    c. Use your equation to determine how many weeks have passed if the plant is 29 inches tall.

Lesson 18 ~ Writing Linear Equations from Key Information

Write an equation in slope-intercept form when given key information about a line.

12. slope $= \frac{3}{4}$, y-intercept $= 5$

13. slope $= -5$, y-intercept $= 1$

14. slope $= 1$, y-intercept $= 9$

15. slope $= \frac{2}{5}$, y-intercept $= 0$

16. slope $= 2$, goes through the point (2, 3)

17. slope $= \frac{1}{2}$, goes through the point (6, 1)

18. slope $= -1$, goes through the point (−3, 5)

19. slope $= \frac{5}{2}$, goes through the point (−6, −10)

20. goes through the points (1, 1) and (5, 9)

21. goes through the points (−6, 0) and (3, 3)

22. goes through the points (−4, 8) and (−3, 5)

23. goes through the points (8, −4) and (5, −4)

24. A furniture rental company rents large screen televisions. They charge an initial fee plus $20 for each day the TV is rented. Steven rented the TV for 8 days and was charged $225. Let x represent the number of days and y represent the total cost of the rental.

    a. Identify the slope and one ordered pair from the information given.

    b. Find the equation of the line that fits this information.

    c. If another customer rents the TV for 17 days, how much should he expect to pay?

25. A canoe rental company on Deep Sea Lake rents canoes for a set fee plus an additional charge per hour. Marshall asked two different individuals how many hours they had rented their canoes for and how much it cost. One rented a canoe for 4 hours and paid $32. Another person rented a canoe for 10 hours for $56. Let x represent the length of time in hours and let y represent the total cost.

    a. Write two ordered pairs that use the data Marshall collected.

    b. Find the equation of the line that goes through these two points.

    c. What number in the linear equation represents the amount of the set fee?

    d. What is the real world meaning of the slope in this equation?

    e. How much will someone pay for a canoe rental from this company if she keeps the canoe for 6 hours?

Lesson 19 ~ Different Forms of Linear Equations

Convert each equation to slope-intercept form.

26. $y = 4 + 2(x - 7)$

27. $3x + 6y = 18$

28. $y = \frac{1}{4}(x + 4) - 3$

29. $4x - 5y = 15$

30. $-x + 3y = -12$

31. $y - 2 = 3(x + 1)$

Lesson 20 ~ More Graphing Linear Equations

Convert each equation to slope-intercept form and graph. Clearly mark at least three points on each line.

32. $-4x + 2y = -6$

33. $y + 1 = 3(x - 2)$

34. $y = \frac{3}{2}(x - 4) + 2$

35. $7x = -14$

36. $x + 3y = 12$

37. $y = 2(x - 1) + 2$

Determine if each point is on the given line.

38. Is the point $(-2, 1)$ on the line $4x - 3y = -11$?

39. Is the point $(2, 5)$ on the line $y = 2(x - 1) + 3$?

40. Is the point $(-6, 0)$ on the line $y + 4 = \frac{1}{2}(x + 4) + 3$?

Lesson 21 ~ Introduction to Non-Linear Functions

Determine if each graph, table or equation is linear or non-linear. If it is non-linear, identify the type of graph (quadratic, exponential or inverse variation).

41.

x	y
−2	12
−1	3
0	0
1	3
2	12

42. $y = \frac{2}{3}x - 4$

43.

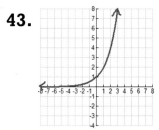

44.

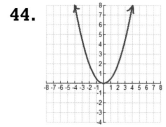

45.

x	y
−2	0
−1	2
0	4
1	6
2	8

46.

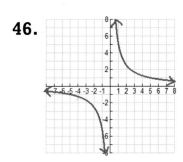

SCOTT
RETAIL MANAGER
DALLAS, OREGON

I am a retail manager for a department store. My position plays an important part in making sure that our department makes money. Many decisions that I make affect how much money our department brings in. I try to maximize our profits by making sure that our products are good and are priced right. I also determine how many employees to hire and how many should work each day. If too many people are working, profits get spent on labor we do not need.

I use math every day in my job as a retail manager. I use basic math skills in my job as well as complex equations. Math helps me to determine how to get the most profits for the department. The profit of my department is affected by "shrink." Shrink is a term that we use in retail to describe theft, damaged or broken products, and products that we never received but still get billed for. Profits are also affected by the cost of transportation, electricity, building maintenance and advertising. As a retail manager, I can control how many employees we are using and also reduce shrink. Both of these things will improve the company's total profits.

I was hired as a retail manager after I had completed my college degree. A person can get hired in my career with a high school diploma, but will need to go through lots of on the job training. People usually have to work their way up through the company to get into a management position.

Salaries for retail managers can vary quite a bit. Salaries start as low as minimum wage for people without experience or other training. People who get into a management training program can earn around $25,000 per year. After becoming a manager, salaries range from $40,000 to $60,000 per year.

I like my job as a retail manager because I enjoy working with the public. I also like how fast things change in the retail world. The best part of my job, though, is helping new employees turn into great long-term members of our team.

BLOCK 4 ~ LINEAR EQUATIONS

SYSTEMS OF EQUATIONS

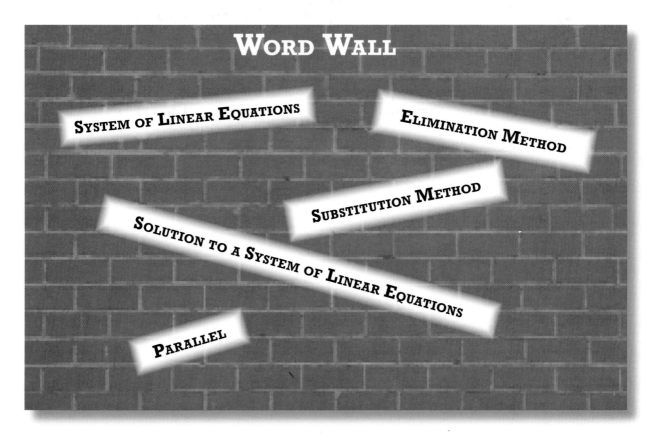

WORD WALL

SYSTEM OF LINEAR EQUATIONS

ELIMINATION METHOD

SUBSTITUTION METHOD

SOLUTION TO A SYSTEM OF LINEAR EQUATIONS

PARALLEL

BLOCK 4 ~ SYSTEMS OF EQUATIONS
TIC - TAC - TOE

HOW MANY SOLUTIONS?

Determine whether a system of three linear equations has zero, one or infinitely many solutions.

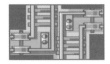

See page 132 for details.

PROS AND CONS

Create a visual display showing the positive and negative aspects of each method for solving systems of equations.

See page 162 for details.

POLYGONS

Develop systems of equations that make different polygons when graphed.

See page 145 for details.

"HOW TO" GUIDE

Produce a brochure about solving systems of linear equations using at least two different ways.

See page 162 for details.

FRACTION COEFFICIENTS

Solve systems of equations with fraction coefficients.

See page 158 for details.

MATH DICTIONARY

Make a dictionary for all the vocabulary terms in this textbook. Create diagrams when possible.

See page 141 for details.

LETTER TO FIFTH GRADERS

Write a letter to a fifth grade class explaining why learning math is important. Support your reasons with research.

See page 145 for details.

DIFFERENT SYSTEMS

Find the solutions to systems of equations involving a quadratic and a linear function.

See page 141 for details.

SOLUTION GIVEN

Create systems of equations that have given solutions.

See page 149 for details.

PARALLEL, INTERSECTING OR THE SAME LINE

LESSON 22

Algebraically determine if two lines are parallel, intersecting or the same line.

In this block, you will look at two linear equations at the same time. A set of two or more linear equations that have common variables is called a system of linear equations. Systems of linear equations have three different types of linear relationships.

EXPLORE!   **TYPES OF SYSTEMS**

System #1	System #2	System #3
$y = \frac{1}{2}x - 2$	$y = -3 + 4x$	$y = -\frac{2}{3}x - 1$
$6x + 2y = 10$	$y = 4(x + 1) - 7$	$2x + 3y = 6$

Step 1: For each system, convert all equations into slope-intercept form.

Step 2: Draw three coordinate planes. Graph the two lines in System #1 on the first coordinate plane, graph System #2 on the second coordinate plane and System #3 on the third coordinate plane.

Step 3: Describe in words how the two lines in System #1 are related.

Step 4: Describe in words how the two lines in System #2 are related.

Step 5: Describe in words how the two lines in System #3 are related.

Step 6: Is there a way to tell, just by looking at the equations in slope-intercept form, when the lines will be intersecting, parallel or the same line? Explain.

Step 7: Without graphing, how do you think the equations in System #4 are related? Explain your answer.

System #4
$y = 5x - 1$
$y = 5x + 4$

A **solution to a system of linear equations** is the ordered pair (x, y) that satisfies both linear equations in the system. The solution to the system of linear equations is found at the point of intersection of the two lines. Systems of linear equations can have one solution, no solutions or infinitely many solutions.

Solution →

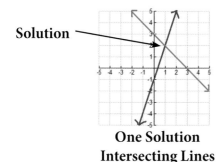

One Solution
Intersecting Lines

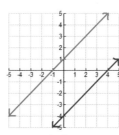

No Solution
Parallel Lines

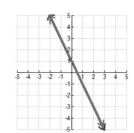

Infinitely Many Solutions
Same Line

A set of two lines that intersects has one solution. A set of two lines that are **parallel** has no solutions because parallel lines never intersect. If a system of linear equations contains two equations that represent the same line, there are infinitely many solutions because the two lines intersect at an infinite number of points.

If the linear equations are in slope-intercept form, it is possible to determine whether the two lines are intersecting, parallel or the same lines just by looking at their slopes and y-intercepts.

DETERMINING TYPES OF SYSTEMS

1. If the two lines have the SAME slope and SAME y-intercept, the two lines are the same line.
2. If the two lines have the SAME slope but DIFFERENT y-intercepts, the lines are parallel.
3. If the two lines have DIFFERENT slopes, the lines are intersecting.

EXAMPLE 1

Determine if the two lines in each system of equations are intersecting, parallel or the same lines. State how many solutions there will be for each system.

a. $4x - 5y = 30$
$y = \frac{4}{5}x - 3$

b. $-x + 2y = -6$
$y = \frac{1}{2}(x + 2) - 4$

c. $y = 2x + 1$
$y = -2x + 1$

SOLUTIONS

a. Convert equations to slope-intercept form.

$$4x - 5y = 30$$
$$-4x \qquad\quad -4x$$

$$\frac{-5y}{-5} = \frac{30 - 4x}{-5}$$

$$y = -6 + \frac{4}{5}x \text{ or}$$

$$\boxed{y = \frac{4}{5}x - 6}$$

$$y = \frac{4}{5}x - 3$$

$$\downarrow$$

$$\boxed{y = \frac{4}{5}x - 3}$$

Compare the two equations. The slopes of the two lines are the same but the y-intercepts are different. This means that the two lines are <u>parallel</u>. There are <u>no solutions</u> to this system.

b. Convert both equations to slope-intercept form.

$$-x + 2y = -6$$
$$+x \qquad\quad +x$$

$$\frac{2y}{2} = \frac{x - 6}{2}$$

$$\boxed{y = \frac{1}{2}x - 3}$$

$$y = \frac{1}{2}(x + 2) - 4$$

$$y = \frac{1}{2}x + 1 - 4$$

$$\boxed{y = \frac{1}{2}x - 3}$$

Compare the two equations in slope-intercept form, $y = \frac{1}{2}x - 3$ and $y = \frac{1}{2}x - 3$. The slopes and y-intercepts of the two lines are the same. This means that the lines two are the <u>same line</u> and there are <u>infinitely many solutions</u> to this system.

c. Both equations are already in slope-intercept form. The equations have different slopes, therefore the two lines are <u>intersecting</u>. There is <u>one solution</u>.

EXERCISES

Determine if each graph shows a system of linear equations that is intersecting, parallel or the same line. State how many solutions there are for each system.

1.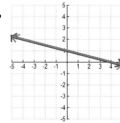

2.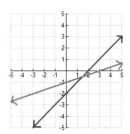

3.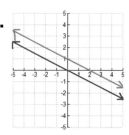

Graph the two linear equations in each system on a single coordinate plane. State whether the lines are intersecting, parallel or the same line.

4. $y = -3x$
  $y = \frac{1}{3}x + 3$

5. $y = 3 + \frac{1}{2}x$
  $y = \frac{1}{2}x + 3$

6. $y = 1 + 4(x - 1)$
  $y = 4(x + 1) + 1$

Determine if the two lines in each system of equations are intersecting, parallel or the same lines by comparing the linear equations in slope-intercept form. State how many solutions there will be for each system.

7. $y = -3x + 4$
  $y = -3x + 3$

8. $y = -\frac{2}{3}x + 5$
  $y = 3x - 5$

9. $2y = -4x + 12$
  $y = 2x + 4$

10. $y = \frac{1}{3}x - 2$
  $-3x + 6y = -12$

11. $6y = 15$
  $10y = 25$

12. $6x + y = 5$
  $y = 6x - 3$

13. Two ants crawled across a piece of graph paper. One followed the path of the linear equation $3x + 2y = 8$. The other ant followed the path of the linear equation $2x + 3y = 6$. Will the ants' paths cross? How do you know?

14. A parallelogram was formed by the intersection of the four lines whose equations are given. Determine algebraically which pairs of sides ($\overline{AB}$, $\overline{BC}$, $\overline{CD}$, $\overline{DA}$) are parallel. Graph the four equations to verify your answer.
  $\overline{AD}$: $2x + 3y = 6$
  $\overline{AB}$: $-6x + 4y = 0$
  $\overline{BC}$: $y = -\frac{2}{3}x + 4$
  $\overline{CD}$: $y = -5 + \frac{3}{2}x$

15. Kirk and Samantha walk home from school. The map of their town was placed on a coordinate grid. Kirk walked home following the linear equation $5x + 4y = 28$. Samantha walked home following the path of $y = -\frac{5}{4}x + 7$. Describe the similarities or differences in their paths home.

16. Write a system of two linear equations in which the lines will intersect. Graph the two lines on the same coordinate plane.

17. Write a system of two linear equations in which the lines are parallel. Graph the two lines on the same coordinate plane.

18. Describe how you can tell if two lines intersect by looking at the linear equations in slope-intercept form.

19. On her Block 4 Test, Victoria was asked to give an example of two lines that are parallel but not the same line. She answered with the equations: $y = 4x + 5$ and $y = 3x + 5$. Did she get the question right? If not, what mistake did she make?

REVIEW

State whether each equation is true or false for the values of the variables given.

20. $5x + 2y = 10$ where $x = 0$ and $y = 5$

21. $-3x + y = 7$ where $x = -1$ and $y = -4$

22. $y = \frac{4}{3}x - 2$ where $x = 9$ and $y = 34$

23. $y = 1 + 2(x - 5)$ where $x = 7$ and $y = 5$

Simplify each expression.

24. $4 + 6x - 1 + 2x$

25. $3(x - 2) + 2(x + 7)$

26. $5x + x + 7x - 10x$

27. $6(x - 1) - 2(x + 1)$

28. $7x + 3y - x + 4y - 2x$

29. $3(2x + 4y) + 5(x - 2y)$

TIC-TAC-TOE ~ HOW MANY SOLUTIONS?

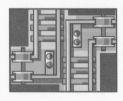

In this block, all the systems of linear equations only include two equations. Systems of equations can include more than two equations. A solution to a system of linear equations is the point where all the lines intersect. Each of the systems below has either zero, one or infinitely many solutions. Use input-output tables or graphing to determine the number of solutions. If the system does have one solution, give the point of intersection.

SYSTEM #1

$y = 3x + 3$
$y = 3x - 4$
$y = 3x - 7$

SYSTEM #2

$y = 2(x - 3) + 5$
$4x - 2y = 2$
$y = 2x - 1$

SYSTEM #3

$y = \frac{1}{2}x - 3$
$y = x - 5$
$y = -\frac{3}{4}x + 2$

SYSTEM #4

$y = \frac{1}{2}x$
$-x + 2y = 6$
$y = \frac{1}{2}(x + 4) - 1$

SYSTEM #5

$y + x = 6$
$2x + y = 8$
$-x + y = 2$

Determine the solution to a system of equations by graphing.

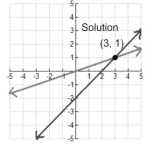

Systems of linear equations can have zero, one or infinitely many solutions. A solution to a system of linear equations is the ordered pair (x, y) that satisfies both linear equations in the system. The solution is the point(s) where the two lines intersect. The solution is stated by giving the coordinates for the point(s) where the two lines intersect.

It is important to always check your solution by verifying that the ordered pair (x, y) creates a true statement when substituted into each linear equation in the system.

EXAMPLE 1

Sue graphed the following systems. She listed her solution to each system below. Decide whether her ordered pair is a solution to the system of equations.

a. $-2x + 4y = 20$
$3x + y = -9$
Sue's Answer: $(-4, 3)$

b. $y = \frac{1}{3}x + 3$
$x + y = 9$
Sue's Answer: $(-9, 0)$

SOLUTIONS

a. Substitute -4 for x and 3 for y in each linear equation in the system.

$$-2x + 4y = 20 \qquad\qquad 3x + y = -9$$
$$-2(-4) + 4(3) \overset{?}{=} 20 \qquad 3(-4) + 3 \overset{?}{=} -9$$
$$8 + 12 \overset{?}{=} 20 \qquad\qquad -12 + 3 \overset{?}{=} -9$$
$$20 = 20 \qquad\qquad\qquad -9 = -9$$

The ordered pair makes each equation true. It is a solution to the system of linear equations.

b. Substitute -9 for x and 0 for y in each linear equation in the system.

$$y = \frac{1}{3}x + 3 \qquad\qquad x + y = 9$$
$$0 \overset{?}{=} \frac{1}{3}(-9) + 3 \qquad -9 + 0 \overset{?}{=} 9$$
$$0 \overset{?}{=} -3 + 3 \qquad\qquad -9 \neq 9$$
$$0 = 0$$

The ordered pair works in the first equation but does not work in the second equation. It is NOT the solution to the system of linear equations.

SOLVING SYSTEMS OF LINEAR EQUATIONS BY GRAPHING
1. Convert both linear equations in the system to slope-intercept form.
2. Graph both equations on the same coordinate plane. Be sure to clearly mark at least three points on each line.
3. Determine the point of intersection.
4. Verify that the ordered pair is the solution by substituting the *x*-values and *y*-values into each equation in the system.

EXAMPLE 2

Solve the system of equations by graphing. Check the solution.

$$y = \tfrac{1}{2}x - 3 \qquad \text{and} \qquad 3x + 2y = 2$$

SOLUTION

Convert both equations to slope-intercept form.

$$y = \tfrac{1}{2}x - 3 \qquad\qquad 3x + 2y = 2$$
$$\underline{\,-3x \qquad -3x}$$
$$\frac{2y}{2} = \frac{-3x + 2}{2}$$

$$\boxed{y = \tfrac{1}{2}x - 3} \qquad\qquad \boxed{y = -\tfrac{3}{2}x + 1}$$

Graph both equations on the same coordinate plane. Start at the *y*-intercept and create at least two more points on each line before drawing the lines.

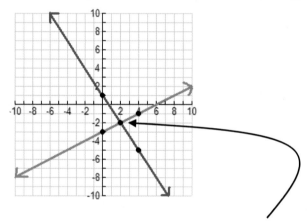

Determine the point of intersection of the two lines → (2, −2).

☑ Check the solution (2, −2) by substituting the 2 in for *x* and −2 in for *y* in each equation to determine if they make the equation true.

$$y = \tfrac{1}{2}x - 3 \qquad\qquad 3x + 2y = 2$$
$$-2 \overset{?}{=} \tfrac{1}{2}(2) - 3 \qquad\qquad 3(2) + 2(-2) \overset{?}{=} 2$$
$$-2 \overset{?}{=} 1 - 3 \qquad\qquad 6 + -4 \overset{?}{=} 2$$
$$-2 = -2 \qquad\qquad 2 = 2$$

The point (2, −2) is the solution to the system.

EXERCISES

1. Al was sick when his math class learned how to solve systems of linear equations by graphing. Explain the process Al needs to follow to find the solution to a system of linear equations by graphing.

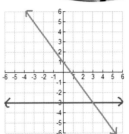

Use each graph to solve the system of linear equations.

2.

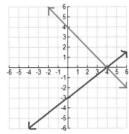

3.

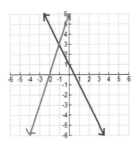

4.

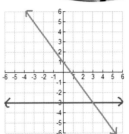

Decide whether the given ordered pair is a solution to the system of equations.

5. $y = -4x$
$y = \frac{1}{2}x + 7$
$(-2, 8)$

6. $x + 5y = 8$
$4x - 5y = 7$
$(3, 1)$

7. $y = x - 9$
$x + y = -1$
$(4, -5)$

8. Polly took a quiz on solving systems of linear equations. She was not sure how she did on two of the harder problems when she turned in the quiz. Later, her friend told her she should have checked her answers. Did Polly answer the questions correctly?

a.
$$y = 4x - 1$$
$$2x - y = -13$$
Polly's solution $(-2, -9)$

b.
$$3x + 6y = 15$$
$$-2x + 3y = -3$$
Polly's solution $(3, 1)$

Solve each system of equations by graphing. Check the solution. If the system does not have exactly one solution, state whether it has no solution or infinitely many solutions.

9. $y = -\frac{1}{4}x + 6$
$y = \frac{1}{2}x + 3$

10. $y = x - 2$
$y = -2x + 1$

11. $y = \frac{1}{2}x + 1$
$y = 4$

12. $y = -\frac{1}{4}x + 1$
$x + 4y = 4$

13. $y = \frac{1}{3}x + 2$
$y = -\frac{2}{3}x + 5$

14. $y = \frac{2}{3}x - 3$
$x = -3$

15. $y = -5 + \frac{3}{2}x$
$-2x + 4y = 4$

16. $y = -3x + 4$
$2x - y = 1$

17. $2x + 5y = 5$
$y = -\frac{2}{5}x + 4$

18. Sarah begins the year with $100 in her savings account. Each week, she spends $8. Martin begins the year with no money saved, but each week he puts $12 into an account. Let x represent the number of weeks and y represent the total money in the account.

    a. Write a linear equation to represent Sarah's total money in her savings based on the number of weeks that have passed.

    b. Write a linear equation to represent Martin's total money in his savings based on the number of weeks that have passed.

    c. Graph both equations on the same first quadrant coordinate plane.

    d. At what point do the lines intersect? What is the real-world meaning of this point?

19. The perimeter of Karen's rectangular garden is 42 feet. The length of the garden is 3 feet more than twice the width. Let y represent the length of the garden and x represent the width of the garden.

    a. Write a linear equation that represents the perimeter of Karen's garden.

    b. Write a linear equation that describes the length of the garden in terms of the width.

    c. Graph both equations on the same coordinate plane.

    d. What are the length and width of Karen's garden?

20. Barry and Helen each own sailboats that are docked in different locations. Both decide to go sailing on Saturday morning and leave at the same time. Barry's sailing path can be described by the linear equation $y = 12x - 30$ and Helen's path can be described by the equation $y = 3x + 60$. At what point will they cross paths?

REVIEW

Determine if the two lines in each system of equations are intersecting, parallel or the same lines by comparing the linear equations in slope-intercept form. State how many solutions there will be for each system.

21. $y = -2x - 5$
    $y = 2x + 1$

22. $4x - 8y = 16$
    $y = \frac{1}{2}x - 2$

23. $y = 5(x + 3) - 1$
    $y = 5x + 7$

24. $y = \frac{2}{3}x - 1$
    $-2x + 3y = 3$

25. $y = \frac{1}{3}x + 3$
    $x + 2y = 6$

26. $y = 3(2x + 1) - 5$
    $y = 6(x - 1) + 4$

SOLVING SYSTEMS USING TABLES

LESSON 24

 Determine the solution to a system of equations using tables.

Input-output tables are a tool used in mathematics to display information. Systems of equations can be solved using tables. An input-output table must be created for each equation in the system. The tables can be compared to find an (x, y) pair that is the same in each table. This point represents the solution to the system of equations.

EXPLORE!

LARRY'S LANDSCAPING

Larry's Landscaping offers two pay options for his employees. Option #1 offers $925 per month in salary plus $25 for every job completed. Option #2 offers $1,000 every month plus $10 for every job completed.

Step 1: Write an equation to represent the monthly salary, y, that could be earned for x jobs completed if an employee chooses Option #1.

Step 2: Write an equation to represent the monthly salary, y, that could be earned for x jobs completed if an employee chooses Option #2.

Step 3: Copy the two tables shown below on your own paper. Calculate the monthly salary for an employee under each plan for 0 through 10 jobs.

Option #1

Jobs Completed, x	Monthly Salary, y
0	
1	
2	

Option #2

Jobs Completed, x	Monthly Salary, y
0	
1	
2	

Step 4: The solution to this system of equations occurs when an employee earns the same amount of money for the same number of jobs. Use your table to determine when this happens. Write your answer in a complete sentence.

Step 5: Verify your answer by substituting the x- and y-values of your solution into the original equations in the system to see if the ordered pair makes each equation true.

Step 6: If an employee thinks he can complete 50 jobs in one month, which job option should he choose? Explain your answer.

SOLVING SYSTEMS OF LINEAR EQUATIONS USING TABLES

1. Convert both linear equations in the system to slope-intercept form.
2. Create an input-output table for each equation. Use the same input values for each table.
3. Locate the point in each table where the same pair of input and output values occurs. This is the solution to the system of equations.
4. Verify that the ordered pair is the solution by substituting the x-and y-values into both equations in the system.

EXAMPLE 1

Solve the system of equations using input-output tables. Check the solution.

$$y = -3x + 13 \qquad\qquad 2x + y = 9$$

SOLUTION

Convert both equations to slope-intercept form:

$$y = -3x + 13 \qquad\qquad 2x + y = 9$$
$$\downarrow \qquad\qquad\qquad \underline{-2x \qquad\quad -2x}$$
$$\boxed{y = -3x + 13} \qquad\qquad \downarrow$$
$$\boxed{y = 9 - 2x}$$

Create an input-output table for each equation using the same input values.

$y = -3x + 13$

x	y
0	13
1	10
2	7
3	4
4	1
5	−2

$y = 9 - 2x$

x	y
0	9
1	7
2	5
3	3
4	1
5	−1

The solution is the ordered pair that occurs in both tables.

The solution to the system of equations is (4, 1).

☑ Verify the answer by substituting 4 for x and 1 for y in the original equations.

$$y = -3x + 13 \qquad\qquad 2x + y = 9$$
$$1 \overset{?}{=} -3(4) + 13 \qquad\qquad 2(4) + 1 \overset{?}{=} 9$$
$$1 \overset{?}{=} -12 + 13 \qquad\qquad 8 + 1 \overset{?}{=} 9$$
$$1 = 1 \qquad\qquad\qquad 9 = 9$$

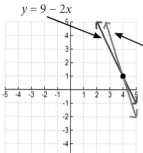

$y = 9 - 2x$

$y = 3x + 13$

A solution to a system of equations that is solved using input-output tables can also be verified using a graph. In **Example 1**, the solution to the system of equations is (4, 1). This means the lines intersect at (4, 1).

EXAMPLE 2

Solve the system of equations using input-output tables. Check the solution.

$$y = \tfrac{1}{2}x + 4 \qquad\qquad y = -x + 1$$

SOLUTION

Both equations are in slope-intercept form. Create an input-output table for each equation using the same input values.

$y = \tfrac{1}{2}x + 4$

x	y
0	4
1	$4\tfrac{1}{2}$
2	5
3	$5\tfrac{1}{2}$

y-values are getting larger.

$y = -x + 1$

x	y
0	1
1	0
2	−1
3	−2

y-values are getting smaller.

The *y*-values are going in opposite directions. The solution must have a negative *x*-value. Use input values that are negative to find the solution.

$y = \tfrac{1}{2}x + 4$

x	y
−1	$3\tfrac{1}{2}$
−2	3
−3	$2\tfrac{1}{2}$
−4	2

$y = -x + 1$

x	y
−1	2
−2	3
−3	4
−4	5

The solution to the system of equations is (−2, 3).

☑ Verify the answer by substituting −2 for *x* and 3 for *y* in the original equations.

$y = \tfrac{1}{2}x + 4$
$3 \overset{?}{=} \tfrac{1}{2}(-2) + 4$
$3 \overset{?}{=} -1 + 4$
$3 = 3$

$y = -x + 1$
$3 \overset{?}{=} -(-2) + 1$
$3 \overset{?}{=} 2 + 1$
$3 = 3$

EXERCISES

Solve each system of equations using the given input-output tables. Check your solution.

1.

$y = 3x - 1$

x	y
0	
1	
2	
3	

$y = -2x + 4$

x	y
0	
1	
2	
3	

2.

$y = x + 6$

x	y
−3	
−2	
−1	
0	

$y = \tfrac{1}{2}x + 5$

x	y
−3	
−2	
−1	
0	

3. Abe created input-output tables with input-values of 0, 1, 2, 3 and 4 to solve his system of equations. After looking at his output values, he realized he needed to try negative input values. What do you think he noticed about his output values?

Solve each system of equations using input-output tables. Check each solution.

4. $y = 5x - 6$
   $y = -2x + 15$

5. $y = x + 2$
   $y = 2x + 1$

6. $y = 3x + 4$
   $y = 2x + 14$

7. $y = \frac{1}{2}x$
   $y = 3x + 10$

8. $2x + y = 3$
   $y - 3x = 23$

9. $-4x + 2y = 12$
   $y = -5x + 6$

10. Two submarines were headed toward one another. One followed the path represented by the equation $y = 4x + 7$. The other submarine followed the path represented by the equation $y = 3x + 12$. Let x represent the number of minutes the submarines have been in motion and y represent the distance each is from the submarine base.

    a. Solve the system of equations using two input-output tables to determine when the submarines paths will cross.

    b. Check your solution by substituting the values into the original equations.

11. Carlos put $100 in a savings account at the beginning of the year. At the end of each month, he added $15 to the account. Ana put $400 in her savings account at the beginning of the year. At the end of each month, she took $35 out of her account. Let x represent the number of months which have passed and y represent the amount in each savings account.

    a. Write an equation to represent the amount in Carlos' savings account.

    b. Write an equation to represent the amount in Ana's savings account.

    c. Copy and complete the input-output tables through 8 months.

Carlos' Savings Account Balance

Months, x	Total Savings, y
0	
1	
2	

Ana's Savings Account Balance

Months, x	Total Savings, y
0	
1	
2	

    d. When will Carlos and Ana have the same amount in their savings accounts? How much will they each have at this time?

12. Solve each system of equations using input-output tables. Verify each solution by graphing the two equations.

    a. $y = \frac{1}{2}x - 1$
       $y = -x + 5$

    b. $y = -2x - 3$
       $y = x - 9$

13. Joshua's profits, P, for his lawn mowing business are represented by the equation $P = 16m - 52$ where m is the number of lawns he has mowed. Serj also runs a lawn-mowing business. His profits can be calculated using the equation $P = 14m - 40$. How many lawns do they have to mow to make the same amount of profit?

Solve each equation. Check the solution.

14. $8x - 10 = -2x + 60$

15. $\frac{2}{3}x + 7 = \frac{4}{3}x + 6$

16. $4x + 2 = 5x + 7$

17. $-2x = 6x + 40$

18. $x + 3 = \frac{1}{2}x + 1$

19. $3.2x - 12 = 4.7x - 9$

TIC-TAC-TOE ~ DIFFERENT SYSTEMS

Systems of equations can include equations that are not linear. In this activity, you will be finding the solutions to systems of equations containing a linear equation and a quadratic equation. Each system will have 2 solutions. You may use graphing or input-output tables to find the solutions.

For example: $y = x + 3$
$y = x^2 - 3$

$y = x + 3$

x	y
-3	0
-2	1
-1	2
0	3
1	4
2	5
3	6

$y = x^2 - 3$

x	y
-3	6
-2	1
-1	-2
0	-3
1	-2
2	1
3	6

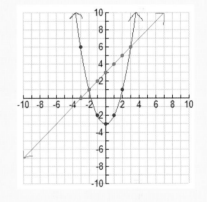

SOLUTIONS: (-2, 1) and (3, 6)

Find the two solutions to each system of equations. Show all work.

1. $y = x^2$
$y = 2x + 3$

2. $y = -x^2 + 1$
$y = x - 5$

3. $y = 3x + 1$
$y = x^2 + 1$

TIC-TAC-TOE ~ MATH DICTIONARY

Create a "Linear Equations" Dictionary. Locate all of the vocabulary words from all four Blocks in this textbook. Alphabetize the list of words and design a dictionary. The dictionary should include each word, spelled correctly, along with the definition. If appropriate, a diagram or illustration can be included.

Determine the solution to a system of equations using the substitution method.

Solving a system of linear equations by graphing or input-output tables is convenient when the ordered pair solution contains only small integers. This will not occur with every system of equations. This lesson shows another method for solving a system of linear equations called the substitution method.

SOLVING SYSTEMS OF LINEAR EQUATIONS BY SUBSTITUTION

1. Solve one of the linear equations for a variable (isolate x or y), if necessary.
2. Replace the variable in the second equation with the expression that you solved for in **Step 1**. Solve for the variable in your new equation.
3. Substitute your solution into the equation from **Step 1** to find the value of the other variable. State your full answer as an ordered pair (x, y).
4. Verify that the ordered pair is the solution by substituting the x- and y-values into both equations in the system or by graphing the system to confirm that the point of intersection matches your solution.

EXAMPLE 1

Use the substitution method to solve the system of linear equations.

$$y = -2x + 5$$
$$4x + 3y = 9$$

SOLUTION

The first equation has an isolated variable. Since $y = -2x + 5$, substitute $-2x + 5$ for y in the second equation and solve for x.

$$4x + 3y = 9$$
$$4x + 3(-2x + 5) = 9$$
$$4x + -6x + 15 = 9$$
$$-2x + 15 = 9$$

$$\begin{array}{r|r} -15 & -15 \\ \hline -2x & -6 \\ \hline -2 & -2 \end{array}$$

$$x = 3$$

> Always put the expression in parentheses because you will often have to use the Distributive Property.

Substitute 3 for x in the first equation.

$$y = -2(3) + 5$$
$$y = -6 + 5$$
$$y = -1$$

Verify that $(3, -1)$ makes both equations true.

$$y = -2x + 5 \qquad\qquad 4x + 3y = 9$$
$$-1 \overset{?}{=} -2(3) + 5 \qquad 4(3) + 3(-1) \overset{?}{=} 9$$
$$-1 \overset{?}{=} -6 + 5 \qquad\qquad 12 + -3 \overset{?}{=} 9$$
$$-1 = -1 \qquad\qquad\qquad 9 = 9$$

Solution: $(3, -1)$

You can also graph the two linear equations to verify that your solution matches the point of intersection. Looking at this graph you can see why substitution was a better method than graphing. It is hard to determine the exact point of intersection on the graph.

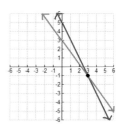

EXPLORE! A TRIP ON HWY. 97

Zach lives in Madras, Oregon. Gina lives 45 miles south in Bend, Oregon. Gina and Zach both leave their houses at the same time, heading south on Highway 97. Zach drives 65 miles per hour and Gina drives 55 miles per hour. Zach wants to determine how long it will take before he catches up with Gina.

Step 1: Copy the equations listed below and identify which equation corresponds to Zach and which equation corresponds to Gina. The y-variable represents the distance from Zach's house. Describe what the x variable represents in this situation.

$$y = 55x + 45$$
$$y = 65x$$

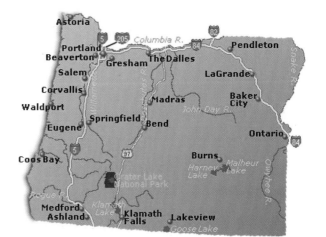

Step 2: Solve this system of equations using the substitution method.

Step 3: How many hours will it take before Zach catches Gina? How far will Zach have driven at this point?

EXERCISES

Identify the equation that has an isolated variable. State which variable is isolated.

1. Equation #1 $3x - 5y = 10$
    Equation #2 $x = 4 - 4y$

2. Equation #1 $y = \frac{1}{2}x - 4$
    Equation #2 $x - 5y = 5$

3. Equation #1 $-x + 3y = 10$
    Equation #2 $y = 4 - 2x$

4. Equation #1 $12 - 6y = x$
    Equation #2 $2x + y = 6$

5. Nathan wants to know why he cannot always just use graphing to solve a system of linear equations. How would you answer his question?

6. Explain the two methods you could use to check your answer when using the substitution method.

Solve each system of equations using the substitution method. Check the solution.

7. $x = y - 3$
$5x + 3y = 1$

8. $3x - y = 7$
$y = 2x - 4$

9. $y = 10 - 2x$
$3x - 2y = 22$

10. $x = 12 + 3y$
$2x + 5y = -20$

11. $y = 15 + x$
$2x + 5y = 26$

12. $5y + 7x = 2$
$x = 2 + y$

13. $y = -5 + x$
$-2x + y = -4$

14. $2x + 3y = 17$
$2x + y = 3$

15. $x - 7y = 4$
$3x + y = -10$

16. Hank's Ice Cream Shop sells single and double scoop cones. The single scoop cones cost $2.00 and the double scoop cones cost $2.50. In one day he sold 230 cones for a total of $498 in sales.

   a. Explain why the equations $x + y = 230$ and $2x + 2.5y = 498$ represent this situation.

   b. What does x represent in the equations in **part a**? What does y represent?

   c. Isolate one variable in an equation. Solve the system of equations using the substitution method.

   d. What is the real-world meaning of the solution to the system?

17. Emma picked two numbers, x and y. She told her teacher that the sum of the two numbers was 46 and the difference of the two numbers was 12.

   a. Write two different linear equations that model what Emma told her teacher.

   b. Isolate one variable in an equation. Solve the system of linear equations using the substitution method. What were the two numbers Emma picked?

18. The Flying W Ranch raises only cows and horses. There are a total of 340 animals on the ranch. The owner prefers horses over cows so he has 52 more horses than cows.

   a. Write two different linear equations to model this situation.

   b. Solve the system of linear equations using the substitution method. How many horses live at the Flying W Ranch?

19. Tad and Timothy went to the paint store together. Tad bought 6 cans of paint and 1 paint brush for $67. Timothy bought 4 cans of the same paint and 3 of the same type of paint brushes. Timothy's total cost was $54.

   a. Write a linear equation that represents Tad's purchase and another to represent Timothy's purchase. Let x represent the cost of a can of paint and y represent the cost of a paint brush.

   b. Solve the system of linear equations using the substitution method.

   c. What was the cost for a can of paint? The cost of a paint brush?

Determine if the two lines in each system of equations are intersecting, parallel or the same lines. State how many solutions there will be for each system.

20. $y = \frac{4}{5}x + 3$
$\quad y = \frac{4}{5}x - 3$

21. $y = \frac{1}{2}x + 5$
$\quad y = -\frac{1}{2}x + 5$

22. $y = 2(x + 1)$
$\quad y = 2x + 1$

23. $4x + 2y = 30$
$\quad y = \frac{4}{3}x - 5$

24. $-x + 6y = 6$
$\quad y = \frac{1}{6}x + 1$

25. $y = 6(x + 1) - 4$
$\quad 6x - y = 2$

TIC-TAC-TOE ~ LETTER TO FIFTH GRADERS

The Oregon Core Math Standards shift from a focus on calculations in elementary years to a focus on introductory algebra concepts at the sixth, seventh and eighth grade levels. Write a letter to a class of fifth grade students explaining why it is important to learn math. Support your reasons with research. Give some examples of real-world situations in which they will encounter math. Include any advise you believe would help them be successful in mathematics through the middle school years. Turn in one copy of the letter to your teacher and give another copy of the letter to a fifth grade teacher in your district.

TIC-TAC-TOE ~ POLYGONS

Polygons are enclosed figures whose sides are made up of line segments. Create a polygon (triangle, quadrilateral, pentagon, hexagon, etc) by graphing linear equations that enclose the polygon. Write the equations for each line. List the vertices (or points of intersection). Color in the polygon. Repeat the process on another sheet of graph paper, creating a different polygon.

SOLVING SYSTEMS USING ELIMINATION

LESSON 26

Determine the solution to a system of equations using the elimination method.

So far in this block, you have used three methods to solve systems of linear equations: graphing, tables and the substitution method. There are times when both equations in a system may be in standard form $(Ax + By = C)$. When this occurs, the easiest method to use to solve the system will be the **elimination method**. The elimination method involves combining the two equations in a way that will "eliminate" one of the variables so that you can solve for the remaining variable.

SOLVING SYSTEMS OF LINEAR EQUATIONS BY ELIMINATION

1. Arrange the equations so the common variables are lined up vertically in columns and the constants are alone on one side of the equals sign.
2. Multiply one or both equations so that one of the variables (x or y) have coefficients that are opposites.
3. Add the columns together. One variable should cancel out by adding to zero. Solve for the remaining variable.
4. Substitute your solution into either of the original equations and solve for the other variable.
5. Verify that the ordered pair is the solution by substituting the x- and y-values into both equations in the system or by graphing the system to confirm that the point of intersection matches your solution.

EXAMPLE 1

Use the elimination method to solve the system of linear equations.
$$3x - 2y = 1$$
$$2x + 2y = 4$$

SOLUTION

The equations are arranged properly with the variables lined up vertically.

$$3x - 2y = 1$$
$$2x + 2y = 4$$

The equations have y-variables that have coefficients of 2 and −2. These are opposites so y is the variable that will be eliminated.

Add the columns together.
The y-variable is eliminated.
Solve for the remaining variable, x.

Substitute the value of x into one of the original equations.

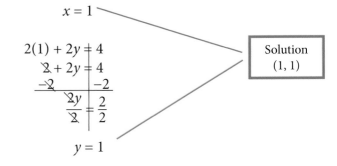

EXAMPLE 1
SOLUTION
(CONTINUED)

☑ Verify that (1, 1) satisfies both equations.

$$3x - 2y = 1 \qquad\qquad 2x + 2y = 4$$
$$3(1) - 2(1) \overset{?}{=} 1 \qquad\qquad 2(1) + 2(1) \overset{?}{=} 4$$
$$3 - 2 \overset{?}{=} 1 \qquad\qquad 2 + 2 \overset{?}{=} 4$$
$$1 = 1 \qquad\qquad 4 = 4$$

EXAMPLE 2

Use the elimination method to solve the system of linear equations.
$$3x + y = 7$$
$$2x + 5y = 22$$

SOLUTION

The equations are arranged properly
with the variables lined up vertically.
$$3x + y = 7$$
$$2x + 5y = 22$$

Neither the x- or y-terms have equal coefficients that are opposites of each other.
In order for the x-coefficients to be equal in amount and opposites, both equations
would have to be multiplied by constants (the first by 2 and the second by −3). The
y-coefficients are easier to make opposites since only one equation had to be multiplied
by a constant. Multiply one equation through by a constant that will create opposites.

$$3x + y = 7 \quad \rightarrow \quad -5(3x + y = 7) \quad \rightarrow \quad -15x + -5y = -35$$
$$2x + 5y = 22 \quad \rightarrow \qquad\qquad\qquad\qquad \rightarrow \qquad 2x + 5y = 22$$

> Choose −5 so the coefficients of
> the y-variables are opposites.

Add the columns together. The y-variable
is eliminated. Solve for the remaining variable.

$$-15x + -5y = -35$$
$$\underline{2x + 5y = 22}$$
$$\frac{-13x}{-13} \frac{-13}{-13}$$

$$x = 1$$

Substitute the value of x into
one of the original equations.
$$3(1) + y = 7$$
$$3 + y = 7$$
$$\underline{-3 -3}$$
$$y = 4$$

Solution
(1, 4)

Verify that (1, 4) satisfies both equations.

$$3x + y = 7 \qquad\qquad 2x + 5y = 22$$
$$3(1) + 4 \overset{?}{=} 7 \qquad\qquad 2(1) + 5(4) \overset{?}{=} 22$$
$$3 + 4 \overset{?}{=} 7 \qquad\qquad 2 + 20 \overset{?}{=} 22$$
$$7 = 7 \qquad\qquad 22 = 22$$

There are three types of steps to follow when trying to get a system of equations ready for "eliminating" a variable.

ZERO-STEP: There is one variable in each equation whose coefficients are equal and one is positive and one is negative.

$$x - 2y = 2$$
$$x + 2y = 10$$

> When the equations are added together, the y terms will cancel.

ONE-STEP: Neither set of variables have opposite coefficients but one term is a multiple of its corresponding variable.

> The x term in the bottom equation is a multiple of the x term in the first equation. Both are positive so multiply the top equation through by -4.

$$x + 3y = -12 \;\to\; -4(x + 3y = -12) \;\to\; -4x - 12y = 48$$
$$4x - 5y = 37 \;\to\; \qquad\qquad\qquad \to\; 4x - 5y = 37$$

SPECIAL TYPE OF ONE-STEP: There is one variable in each equation whose coefficients are equal, not opposites.

> The x terms match but they are both positive. Multiply one equation by -1 and distribute.

$$3x + 3y = -3 \;\to\; -1(3x + 3y = -3) \;\to\; -3x - 3y = 3$$
$$3x + 2y = -1 \;\to\; \qquad\qquad\qquad \to\; 3x + 2y = -1$$

TWO-STEP: Neither set of variables have opposite coefficients. In order to get opposite coefficients on one variable, both equations must be multiplied by different numbers.

> Either variable could be chosen to eliminate in this system (y was chosen because one was positive and one was negative). Multiply each equation through in order to reach the least common multiple.

$$2x - 5y = 7 \;\to\; 2(2x - 5y = 7) \;\to\; 4x - 10y = 14$$
$$3x + 2y = 20 \;\to\; 5(3x + 2y = 20) \;\to\; 15x + 10y = 100$$

EXERCISES

Identify which variable would be easiest to "eliminate" in each system of linear equations. Explain whether it is a 0-step, 1-step or 2-step problem and what multiplication, if any, would have to be completed before the specified variable could be "eliminated".

1. $x + 4y = 23$
$-x + y = 2$

2. $2x + 3y = 13$
$x - 2y = 2$

3. $5x + 2y = 6$
$9x + 2y = 22$

4. $2x + y = 4$
$5x + 4y = 7$

5. $3x + 2y = 8$
$2x - 3y = -12$

6. $2x + 7y = -3$
$x + y = -4$

7. Alexandra wants to eliminate the x-variable in the system below. She multiplies the first equation by 3 and the second equation by 5. She adds the two equations together and the x-variables are still there. What did she do wrong?

$$5x + 3y = 10 \longrightarrow 15x + 9y = 30$$
$$3x + 5y = 14 \qquad 15x + 25y = 70 \longrightarrow 30x + 34y = 100$$

Solve each system of equations using the elimination method. Check the solution.

8. $x + y = 11$
$x - y = -3$

9. $3x + 2y = 0$
$-3x + y = 9$

10. $5x + 2y = -5$
$-x + 3y = 1$

11. $6x - 2y = 36$
$3x - 2y = 21$

12. $3x + y = -11$
$4x - 3y = 7$

13. $5x + 2y = -1$
$x - 2y = 1$

14. $7x - 4y = 26$
$5x + 4y = 46$

15. $12x + 3y = 12$
$8x - 2y = 4$

16. $3x + 4y = -25$
$2x - 3y = 6$

17. Two children's blocks are chosen. Three times the value of one block plus the value of the second block is 29. The value of the first block plus twice the value of the second block is 18.

    a. Write two equations using the information given about the two chosen blocks to create a system of linear equations.

    b. Solve the system of equations using the elimination method. What is the value of each chosen block?

18. Irina sells two types of candy bars for a fund raiser. One type costs $1 and the other costs $2. At the end of the fund raiser, she has sold 44 candy bars for a total of $68. She wants to determine the number of each type of candy bar she has sold. Let x represent the number of $1 candy bars she has sold and y represent the number of $2 candy bars she has sold.

    a. Explain why the equations $x + y = 44$ and $x + 2y = 68$ represent this situation.

    b. Solve the system of equations using the elimination method.

    c. How many $1 candy bars did she sell? How many $2 candy bars did she sell?

REVIEW

Solve each system of linear equations using the graphing method.

19. $y = \frac{4}{5}x - 2$
$y = -\frac{2}{5}x + 4$

20. $y = x - 1$
$y = -3x - 5$

21. $y = -\frac{1}{2}x + 2$
$y = \frac{1}{2}x - 2$

Solve each system of linear equations using the substitution method.

22. $4x + 3y = 31$
$x = 2y + 5$

23. $x = 15 + 12y$
$2x + 3y = 3$

24. $2x + 5y = -1$
$x + y = 4$

 **TIC-TAC-TOE ~ SOLUTION GIVEN**

 Below are solutions to systems of two linear equations. Create a system of linear equations that has each solution. You may not use any horizontal or vertical lines. Prove that your system of equations has the solution by solving the system using graphing, tables, substitution or elimination.

    1. (3, 2)

    2. (0, 5)

    3. (−1, 4)

    4. (2, −6)

    5. (−3, −3)

    6. (8, 0)

CHOOSING THE BEST METHOD

LESSON 27

 Choose the best method for solving a given system of equations.

You have learned four different ways to solve a system of linear equations. All four methods work on any problem, but each problem is usually set-up in a way that makes one method of solving easier than the other methods.

A quick review of the four methods you have learned to solve systems of linear equations:

GRAPHING	Graph both equations in slope-intercept form. Identify their point of intersection.
TABLES	Create an input-output table for each equation using the same input values. Locate the point in each table where the same pair of input and output values occur.
SUBSTITUTION	Solve for a variable in one equation and substitute that expression into the other equation. Solve that equation for one variable. Substitute the solution into one of the original equations to solve for the second variable.
ELIMINATION	Create opposite coefficients on one variable in the two equations. Add equations together to eliminate one variable. Solve for the remaining variable. Substitute the solution into one of the original equations to solve for the second variable.

EXPLORE!   **WHAT'S EASIEST?**

Nate and Tabi were given five systems of equations to solve. Their teacher told them each system could be solved using any of the four methods above. For each one, however, there is one method that would be the easiest to use.

System #1
$$3x + y = 12$$
$$-3x + y = 30$$

System #2
$$y = \tfrac{1}{2}x - 5$$
$$y = -x + 1$$

System #3
$$y = 2x + 5$$
$$y = 4x + 5$$

System #4
$$y = 2x + 1$$
$$4x + 5y = -9$$

System #5
$$2x - 3y = 12$$
$$x = 2y + 8$$

Step 1: Tabi likes elimination the best so she decides that she will solve them all with elimination. Her teacher said one of the systems is set up for elimination. Which system do you think the teacher referred to? Why?

Step 2: Nate believes substitution is always the easiest method to use, no matter how the system is set up. The teacher told Nate there are two systems set up in a way that will make substitution the easiest method for solving. Which two systems do you think the teacher was talking about and why?

Step 3: Two systems are left. Which one would you solve by graphing? Which one would you solve using input-output tables? Explain your reasoning.

Step 4: Choose one of the systems above and find the solution.

CHOOSING A METHOD TO SOLVE A SYSTEM OF LINEAR EQUATIONS

Graphing: If both equations are in slope-intercept form, graphing is an appropriate method to use.

Tables: If both equations are in slope-intercept form and the slope is an integer, input-output tables may be a good method.

Substitution: If a variable is isolated in one equation, substitution will most likely be the best method.

Elimination: If the two equations in the system are in standard form and the variables are lined up in columns, elimination may be the easiest method.

EXAMPLE 1

Choose the best method to solve each system of linear equations. Explain your reasoning.

a. $x - 2y = 10$
$3x + 2y = 6$

b. $y = 2x - 3$
$4x - 5y = -1$

c. $y = \frac{1}{3}x$
$y = 2x + 7$

d. $y = 5x - 9$
$y = 2x - 3$

SOLUTIONS

a. The best method for solving this system of linear equations would be **ELIMINATION**. This method would be easiest because the variables are already lined up in columns and the y–variable is already set to be eliminated when the two equations are added together.

b. The best method for this system is **SUBSTITUTION**. The y-variable in the first equation is isolated on one side of the equals sign which provides an expression to substitute into the other equation and solve.

c. Both equations are solved for y which allows this to be easily solved by **GRAPHING**. Remember that when the graphing method is used, it is important to verify the solution by substituting the x-and y-values back into both equations.

d. Both equations are in slope-intercept form. The slope in each equation is an integer. The best method for solving this system of equations may be **TABLES**.

EXERCISES

Choose the best method to solve each system of linear equations. Explain your reasoning.

1. $3x + y = 13$
$-3x - 4y = -7$

2. $x = 4y$
$3x + 2y = 11$

3. $y = 3x - 7$
$y = -\frac{3}{2}x + 2$

4. Lucy chose to use the graphing method to solve the system of equations shown below. Her friend, Dave, argues that graphing is not the best method. He says he would use tables. Who do you agree with and why?

$$y = 40x + 290$$
$$y = 500 + 25x$$

State the best method to solve each system of linear equations. Solve the system.

5. $3x - y = 14$
$x + y = 2$

6. $x = y + 3$
$2x + 3y = 1$

7. $-4x + 2y = -6$
$2x - 5y = -9$

8. $y = 2x - 4$
$y = x + 1$

9. $y = \frac{1}{2}x + 3$
$3x - 4y = -10$

10. $y = \frac{1}{2}x + 3$
$y = -3x - 4$

11. $3x + 2y = -18$
$-2x + 5y = -26$

12. $y = -\frac{3}{2}x + 5$
$y = 2x - 9$

13. $y = 5x - 2.5$
$4x + 2y = 9$

REVIEW

14. Listed below are six linear equations related to the line $y = \frac{2}{3}x - 4$. Two of the lines are parallel to this line. Two of the lines are the exact same line. The other two intersect the line. Determine which lines fit in each category.

INTERSECTING?

Line A
$-3x + 2y = 6$

Line C
$y = \frac{2}{3}(x + 3) - 6$

Line B
$y = \frac{2}{3}x + 4$

Line D
$4x - 6y = 24$

Line F
$y = -\frac{2}{3}x - 4$

THE SAME LINE?

Line E
$y = \frac{2}{3}(x + 6) - 5$

PARALLEL?

APPLICATIONS OF SYSTEMS OF EQUATIONS

LESSON 28

Set up and solve systems of equations from word problems.

Systems of linear equations are used to solve problems in all types of real-world situations. In this lesson, you will see systems of linear equations used to solve problems involving cell phone plans, job options and shipping costs. You will be given details about a problem that will provide you with enough information to write two linear equations. You must first determine what each variable represents. Once the two linear equations are developed, you must determine which method you want to use to solve the system. Always remember to check your answer by referring back to the original problem to see if your solution is correct.

EXPLORE!

AT THE MOVIES

The Rodriguez family and the Jacobson family go to the movies together. The Rodriguez family bought 3 adult tickets and 2 child tickets for a total of $29.00. The Jacobson family bought 2 adult tickets and 5 child tickets for a total of $31.25. Let x represent the cost of an adult's ticket and y represent the cost of a child's ticket.

Step 1: Write an equation to represent the Rodriguez family's movie ticket purchase.

Step 2: Write an equation to represent the Jacobson family's movie ticket purchase.

Step 3: Choose the best method for solving this system of equations. Why did you choose that method?

Step 4: Solve your system of linear equations.

Step 5: How much did a child's ticket cost at this movie theater? What was the cost of an adult ticket?

Step 6: Check your answer by determining if your ticket prices give the same totals that were charged to the Jacobson and Rodriguez family.

Step 7: The Chang family also went to see the same movie as the other two families. The Changs bought one adult ticket and 3 children's tickets. What was the total cost for the Chang family to go to the movies?

EXAMPLE 1

Nai is trying to decide between two different cell phone plans. Plan A charges a flat fee of $22 per month plus $0.10 per minute of phone usage. Plan B charges $0.18 per minute with no flat fee.

a. How many minutes would Nai have to use each month for the cell phone plans to cost the same amount? How much would it cost?

b. If Nai figures he will talk 400 minutes on the phone each month, which plan should he choose?

SOLUTIONS

a. Let x represent the minutes talked and y represent the total monthly cost.

Write a system of two linear equations to model this situation.

Plan A: $y = 22 + 0.10x$ **Plan B:** $y = 0.18x$

> Start value of $22 plus $0.10 per minute

> $0.18 per minute

Choose a method and solve the system of equations. Graphing or substitution would work. SUBSTITUTION will work best because it will provide an accurate answer since it is not known if the solution will have integer values.

> Substitute $0.18x$ for y.

Solve the system.

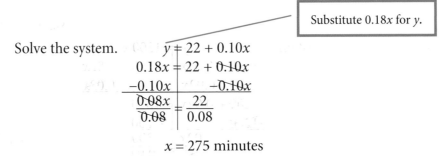

$$y = 22 + 0.10x$$
$$0.18x = 22 + 0.10x$$
$$\underline{-0.10x \qquad\qquad -0.10x}$$
$$\frac{0.08x}{0.08} = \frac{22}{0.08}$$
$$x = 275 \text{ minutes}$$

Substitute the x-value into one of the original equations to determine the total cost when the plans cost the same.

$$y = 0.18(275) = \$49.50$$

The plans would cost the same amount, $49.50, after 275 minutes.

b. Nai plans to talk 400 minutes each month. To determine which plan is best, substitute 400 for x in each equation to see which plan will be less expensive.

Plan A: $y = 22 + 0.10(400) = \$62$
Plan B: $y = 0.18(400) = \$72$

Nai should choose **Plan A** if he plans to use his phone 400 minutes each month.

EXAMPLE 2

Omar has two possible sales job options. Job Option #1 has a monthly salary of $1,200 plus 4% of his total sales. Job Option #2 has a monthly salary of $1,500 plus 2% of his total sales.

a. How much would Omar have to sell to earn the same amount in one month at each job?

b. Omar thinks he can sell an average of $8,000 worth of merchandise in one month. Which job should he take?

SOLUTIONS

a. Let x represent the amount of Omar's sales in one month and y represent the total monthly salary.

Write a system of two linear equations to model this situation.

Job Option #1: $y = 1200 + 0.04x$ ————————
Job Option #2: $y = 1500 + 0.02x$ ————————

| 4% = 0.04 |
| 2% = 0.02 |

Choose a method and solve the system of equations. Graphing or substitution would work. SUBSTITUTION will work best because the y-intercepts are quite large and would be difficult to graph accurately.

Substitute $1200 + 0.04x$ for y

Solve the system:

$$y = 1500 + 0.02x$$
$$1200 + 0.04x = 1500 + 0.02x$$
$$-0.02x \qquad\qquad -0.02x$$
$$\overline{1200 + 0.02x = 1500}$$
$$-1200 \qquad\quad -1200$$
$$\frac{0.02x}{0.02} = \frac{300}{0.02}$$

$$x = \$15,000$$

Substitute the x-value into one of the original equations to determine the total salary when the jobs would pay the same.
$$y = 1200 + 0.04(15000) = \$1,800$$

Omar will earn the same monthly income ($1,800) at **Job Option #1 or #2** if he sells $15,000 worth of merchandise.

b. Use the original equations to determine which job will have the highest pay if he sells $8,000 worth of merchandise. Remember that his sales amount is substituted for x.

Job Option #1: $y = 1200 + 0.04(8000) = \$1,520$
Job Option #2: $y = 1500 + 0.02(8000) = \$1,660$

If Omar sells $8,000 worth of merchandise per month, he should take **Job Option #2.**

EXAMPLE 3

Sunshine Flower Company (SFC) ships boxes of tulip bulbs. The bulbs are always shipped in boxes that are the exact same size and weight. The billing statements are mailed in a separate envelope. On Monday, SFC shipped 210 boxes of bulbs and 140 billing statements. The total shipping bill for the day was $702.10. On Tuesday, SFC shipped 70 boxes of bulbs and 80 billing statements. The total shipping bill for Tuesday was $243.70. Determine the individual cost for mailing a box of bulbs and the cost for mailing a billing statement.

SOLUTION

Let x represent the cost of shipping a box of bulbs and y represent the cost of mailing a billing statement.

Write a system of two linear equations to model this situation.
Monday: $210x + 140y = 702.10$
Tuesday: $70x + 80y = 243.70$

Choose a method and solve the system of equations. This system of equations is set up for using the ELIMINATION method because the x- and y-variables are lined up in columns on one side of the equals sign and the constants are on the other side. Use multiplication in order to get opposite amounts of one variable.

Solve the system by first getting one variable with opposite coefficients.

$$210x + 140y = 702.10 \rightarrow \qquad\qquad \rightarrow \quad 210x + 140y = 702.10$$
$$70x + 80y = 243.70 \quad \rightarrow \quad -3(70x + 80y = 243.70) \rightarrow -210x - 240y = -731.10$$

Add the columns together and solve for y.

$$\begin{aligned} \cancel{210x} + 140y &= 702.10 \\ -\cancel{210x} - 240y &= -731.10 \\ \hline \frac{-100y}{-100} &= \frac{-29}{-100} \end{aligned}$$

$$y = \$0.29$$

Substitute the y-value into one of the original equations to solve for x:

$$\begin{aligned} 70x + 80(0.29) &= 243.70 \\ 70x + 23.20 &= 243.70 \\ -23.20 \qquad &\quad -23.20 \\ \hline \frac{70x}{70} &= \frac{220.50}{70} \end{aligned}$$

$$x = \$3.15$$

Each box of bulbs costs $3.15 to ship. Each billing statement costs $0.29 to mail.

EXERCISES

Develop a system of equations for each problem. Describe what each variable represents.

1. Manny begins the summer with $200 in his savings account. Each week he adds $85 to his account. Susan begins the summer with $95 in a savings account and adds $100 each week. When will Manny and Susan have the same amount of money in their accounts?

2. Travis and Beth went to the corner mini-mart. Travis bought 6 candy bars and 2 sodas for $4.88. Beth bought 2 candy bars and 3 sodas for $3.47. All candy bars cost the same and all sodas are the same price. Determine the price of a candy bar and the price of a soda.

3. Otis will build a fence around his rectangular garden. The perimeter of the garden is 184 feet. The width is two times the length. Find the length and width of his garden. Use the formula for the perimeter of a rectangle as one of your equations.

Develop a system of equations for each problem. Describe what each variable represents. Solve the system and check the solution. Write the answer in a complete sentence.

4. Two taxi companies have different pricing systems. Company A charges a flat fee of $8 plus $0.10 per mile driven. Company B does not charge a flat fee, but charges $0.30 per mile driven. At what distance do both companies charge the same amount?

5. The set-up cost for a machine that attaches snaps on clothing is $1,100. After set-up, it costs $0.12 for each snap to be attached. A newer machine has come out that has a set-up cost of $1,520. With the new machine, it only costs $0.09 for each snap to be attached. How many snaps would the company have to attach to make the purchase of the newer machine worthwhile?

6. Two teachers, Mrs. Wright and Mr. Kinder, decide to buy calculators and protractors for their classrooms. Mrs. Wright buys 40 calculators and 30 protractors for $485. Mr. Kinder buys 20 of each for $252. What are the individual costs of the calculators and protractors that were purchased?

7. Two families had a garage sale together. The entire garage sale brought in $1,640. One family made $182 more than twice as much as the second family. How much did each family make at the garage sale?

8. On Friday night, 560 people went to the local theater. Youth tickets cost $5.75 and adult tickets cost $8.50. If the theater's sales receipts total $3,907.50, how many youth tickets were bought on Friday night?

9. Jeremiah bought 3 gallons of ice cream and 4 containers of strawberries for $19.50. Gary bought 5 gallons of ice cream and 2 containers of strawberries for $22.00. What is the cost of one gallon of ice cream alone? What is the cost of one container of strawberries?

10. Two types of stereos were on sale at a local car stereo dealer. The J-Series model sold for $118. The K-Series model sold for $92. During the sale, 32 stereos were sold. The receipts for these stereos totaled $3,230. How many of each type of stereo did the local dealer sell during this sale?

11. Nancy and Pedro both drove to Portland. Nancy started 72 miles closer to Portland than Pedro did. Her average speed was 50 miles per hour. Pedro left at the same time Nancy left. He averaged 62 miles per hour. How long will it take before Pedro catches up with Nancy?

REVIEW

Decide whether the given ordered pair is a solution to the system of equations.

12. $y = 3x$
$y = \frac{1}{2}x + 7$
$(-2, -6)$

13. $x + 3y = 4$
$4x - 5y = -1$
$(1, 1)$

14. $y = x - 7$
$x + 2y = 14$
$(7, 0)$

Solve the system of equations by graphing. Check the solution. If the system does not have exactly one solution, state whether it has no solution or infinitely many solutions.

15. $y = x - 3$
$y = 2x + 3$

16. $y = \frac{2}{5}x - 2$
$y = -x + 5$

17. $y = \frac{1}{2}x - 1$
$y = 2$

18. $y = -\frac{1}{2}x + 1$
$x + 2y = 2$

19. $y = 1 - \frac{2}{3}x$
$y = \frac{1}{6}x - 4$

20. $-2x + 4y = 8$
$y = \frac{1}{2}x - 3$

TIC-TAC-TOE ~ FRACTION COEFFICIENTS

Each system of linear equations below has at least one fraction coefficient.

Solve each system of linear equations using either substitution or elimination. Show all work.

1. $y = \frac{1}{2}x + 4$
$2x + 4y = 40$

2. $\frac{1}{3}x + 2y = 3$
$x + 3y = 3$

3. $x = 4y - 2$
$\frac{1}{2}x + 5y = 6$

4. $\frac{1}{3}x + \frac{2}{3}y = 0$
$2x + \frac{1}{3}y = -11$

Vocabulary

elimination method	substitution method
parallel	system of linear equations
solution to a system of linear equations	

 Algebraically determine if two lines are parallel, intersecting or the same line.
Determine the solution to a system of equations by graphing.
Determine the solution to a system of equations using tables.
Determine the solution to a system of equations using the substitution method.
Determine the solution to a system of equations using the elimination method.
Choose the best method for solving a given system of equations.
Set up and solve systems of equations from word problems.

Lesson 22 ~ Parallel, Intersecting or The Same Line

Determine if each graph shows a system of linear equations that is intersecting, parallel or the same line. State how many solutions there are for each system.

1.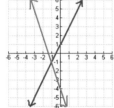

2.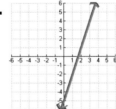

3.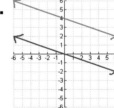

Algebraically determine if the two lines in each system of equations are intersecting, parallel or the same lines by comparing the linear equations in slope-intercept form. State how many solutions there will be for each system.

4. $y = -\frac{1}{2}x - 4$
$y = \frac{1}{2}x + 4$

5. $3x + 4y = 20$
$y = -\frac{3}{4}x - 2$

6. $-6x + 3y = 12$
$y = 2(x + 1) + 2$

Lesson 23 ~ Solving Systems by Graphing

Decide whether the given ordered pair is a solution to the system of equations.

7. $y = 2x - 1$
$y = \frac{1}{3}x + 4$
$(3, 5)$

8. $x - 3y = 4$
$4x + y = -5$
$(-1, 1)$

9. $y = x - 2$
$4x + y = -2$
$(0, -2)$

Solve each system of equations by graphing. Check the solution.

10. $y = \frac{1}{2}x - 3$
$y = x - 5$

11. $y = -2x - 4$
$y = \frac{1}{2}x + 1$

12. $y = -\frac{1}{3}x$
$y = 1$

13. Sandra and Terry each walk to the same school from different neighborhoods. They do not cross paths until they reach the school building. Sandra follows the path represented by the equation $y = -2x + 10$ and Terry follows the path represented by the equation $y = -\frac{1}{6}x - 1$. What are the coordinates of the school building?

Lesson 24 ~ Solving Systems Using Tables
• •

Solve each system of equations using the given input-output tables. Check your solution.

14.

$y = 5x - 4$

x	y
0	
1	
2	
3	

$y = -2x + 3$

x	y
0	
1	
2	
3	

15.

$y = -5 + x$

x	y
−5	
−4	
−3	
−2	

$y = 3x + 3$

x	y
−5	
−4	
−3	
−2	

Solve each system of equations using input-output tables. Check each solution.

16. $y = 3x - 4$
$y = x + 2$

17. $y = -4x + 1$
$y = 2x + 13$

18. $y = x$
$y = 3x - 8$

19. Evan had $400 in a savings account at the beginning of the year. At the end of each month, he took $20 out of the account. Lisa put $100 in her savings account at the beginning of the year. At the end of each month, she put $40 in her account. Let x represent the number of months which have passed and y represent the amount in each savings account.

a. Write an equation to represent the amount in Evan's savings account.
b. Write an equation to represent the amount in Lisa's savings account.
c. Copy and complete the input-output tables through 6 months.

Evan's Savings Account Balance

Months, x	Total Savings, y
0	
1	
2	

Lisa's Savings Account Balance

Months, x	Total Savings, y
0	
1	
2	

d. When will Evan and Lisa have the same amount in their savings accounts? How much will they each have at this time?

• •

Solve the system of equations using the substitution method. Check the solution.

20. $x = y + 1$
$3x + 2y = 18$

21. $-3x + y = 9$
$y = 2x + 6$

22. $x + y = 3$
$x + 2y = 1$

23. Both of Monique's neighbors owned cows. Mr. James owned five less than three times the number of cows owned by Mr. Peters. The total number of cows owned by both neighbors was 79. Let x represent the number of cows Mr. James owns and y represent the number of cows Mr. Peters owns.

   a. Explain why the equations $x = 3y - 5$ and $x + y = 79$ represent this situation.
   b. Solve the system of equations using the substitution method. How many cows did each neighbor own?

• •

Identify which variable would be easiest to "eliminate" in each system of linear equations. Explain whether it is a 0-step, 1-step or 2-step problem and what multiplication, if any, would have to be completed before the specified variable could be "eliminated".

24. $-x + y = 12$
$x + y = 6$

25. $3x - y = 3$
$6x + 2y = 9$

26. $4x + 2y = 9$
$-2x + 3y = 1$

Solve each system of equations using the elimination method. Check the solution.

27. $x + 3y = 17$
$2x - 3y = -20$

28. $5x + 4y = 22$
$2x + 4y = 16$

29. $2x + y = 7$
$4x - 3y = -6$

30. Patrick bought one baseball cap and one t-shirt for $36. Sammy bought two baseball caps identical to Patrick's caps along with three of the same t-shirts. Sammy spent a total of $94.

   a. Explain why the equations $x + y = 36$ and $2x + 3y = 94$ represent this situation.
   b. What does x represent based on the equations in **part a**? What does y represent?
   c. Solve the system of equations using the elimination method. What are the individual costs for a t-shirt and a baseball cap?

• •

State the best method to solve each system of linear equations and then solve.

31. $2x + y = 6$
$x - y = 6$

32. $x = y - 1$
$3x + y = 13$

33. $y = \frac{1}{3}x - 5$
$y = -\frac{4}{3}x$

34. $3x + 4y = 7$
$x - 8y = 0$

35. $y = \frac{1}{2}x + 3$
$-3x + 4y = 18$

36. $y = 2x - 5$
$4x + y = -11$

Describe what each variable represents. Develop a system of equations for each problem. Solve the system and check your solution. Write your answer in a complete sentence.

37. Two jet ski rental companies have different costs. Company A charges a flat fee of $8 plus $2.50 per hour. Company B charges a flat fee of $14 plus $1.00 per hour. At what point in time are both rentals the same amount? How much are the rentals for that amount of time?

38. The Mendenhall Theater sells two types of tickets: youth and adult. The theater holds a total of 450 people. One night, the theater sold all their tickets for a total of $2,706. Youth tickets cost $4.60 and adult tickets cost $7.00. How many tickets of each type did the theater sell that night?

39. Jamal and Emily each started a savings account in January. Jamal started with $46 in his account and added $24 each month. Emily opened her account with $319. Each month she withdrew $15. After how many months will they have the exact same amount in their accounts? How much will be in their accounts at that time?

40. Two girls sold lemonade together. The entire lemonade sale brought in $28. One girl made $4 more than twice the amount the second girl made. How much did each girl make at the lemonade sale?

Tic-Tac-Toe ~ "How To" Guide

 Design a brochure that explains in detail how to solve a system of equations using at least two different methods. Include multiple examples and step-by-step instructions. Include diagrams and helpful hints, when necessary.

Tic-Tac-Toe ~ Pros and Cons

 Four methods for solving systems of linear equations have been introduced in this block. The methods include graphing, input-output tables, elimination and substitution. Create a visual display showing the positive and negative aspects of each method. Describe how a system might be set up in a way that would make one method easier than another. Include an example for each method.

CAREER FOCUS

RYAN
ACCOUNTANT
SALEM, OREGON

My name is Ryan and I am an accountant. Accountants track financial information for businesses and other organizations. This can mean keeping track of data, preparing reports or using numbers to make predictions. Managers and leaders of businesses depend on accountants to give them accurate information so that they can make decisions that best benefit their organization. Accountants also help organizations with figuring out how much money they will need to pay in taxes.

I use math in many ways. I constantly use basic operations to transform raw data into usable information. I have to problem solve in different situations to analyze data for correctness. I also use ratios and fractions to compare how one business is doing as opposed to another. There are a number of types of statistics I use to prepare forecasts and valuations.

A Certified Public Accountant must have a 4-5 year degree in accounting. They must also pass a national exam and have a certain number of hours of on-the-job experience in order to get a license. The on-the-job experience can be done while working under the supervision of a CPA who already has a license.

In the state of Oregon, the starting salary for an accountant is around $36,000 per year. Average salaries range between $43,000 and $67,000 per year depending on the industry and experience level of the accountant. Salaries for accountants can sometimes reach $150,000 per year or more.

I like the many kinds of organizations and industries an accountant can work in. An accountant can work in government, charity or business. They can be entrepreneurs and open their own public accounting firm, or they can work for a Fortune 500 company. They can work in the entertainment industry or in agriculture. Another benefit to working in accounting is always being a key player in the important decisions that shape and direct the organization you work for.

ACKNOWLEDGEMENTS

**All Photos and Clipart ©2008 Jupiterimages Corporation
with the exception of cover photos and the following photos:**

Oregon Focus on Fractions and Decimals Page 16
©iStockphoto.com/Lisa F. Young

Oregon Focus on Fractions and Decimals Page 57
©iStockphoto.com/ericsphotography

Oregon Focus on Fractions and Decimals Page 136
©iStockphoto.com/Andres Balacazar

Oregon Focus on Lines and Angles Page 21
©iStockphoto.com/Juan Monino

Oregon Focus on Data Analysis Page 12
©iStockphoto.com/Amanda Rohole

Oregon Focus on Data Analysis Page 79
©iStockphoto.com/Lisa F. Young

Oregon Focus on Proportionality Page 155
©iStockphoto.com/Amanda Rohole

Layout and Design by JS Data Designs

Design Support by Heather Day

Cover Design by Schuyler St. Lawrence

Glossary Translation by Keyla Santiago

Special thanks to the participants in the Career Focus pages for their willingness to share about their jobs.

Very special thanks to our spouses and families who put up with us during one crazy year of curriculum writing and editing. We couldn't have done it without your support!

GLOSSARY ~ GLOSARIO

A

Absolute Value	The distance a number is from 0 on a number line.	Valor Absoluto	La distancia de un número desde el 0 en una recta numérica.
Acute Angle	An angle that measures more than 0° but less than 90°.	Ángulos Agudos	Un ángulo que mide mas 0° pero menos de 90°.
Adjacent Angles	Two angles that share a ray.	Ángulos Adyacentes	Dos ángulos que comparten un rayo.
Algebraic Expression	An expression that contains numbers, operations and variables.	Expresiones Algebraicas	Una expresión que contiene números, operaciones y variables.
Alternate Exterior Angles	Two angles that are on the outside of two lines and are on opposites sides of a transversal.	Ángulos Exteriores Alternos	Dos ángulos que están afuera de dos rectas y están a lados opuestos de una transversal.
Alternate Interior Angles	Two angles that are on the inside of two lines and are on opposite sides of a transversal.	Ángulos Interiores Alternos	Dos ángulos que están adentro de dos rectas y están a lados opuestos de una transversal.
Angle	A figure formed by two rays with a common endpoint.	Ángulo	Una figura formada por dos rayos con un punto final en común.
Area	The number of square units needed to cover a surface.	Área	El número de unidades cuadradas necesitadas para cubrir una superficie.

Ascending Order	Numbers arranged from least to greatest.	Progresión Ascendente	Los números ordenados de menor a mayor.
Associative Property	A property that states that numbers in addition or multiplication expressions can be grouped without affecting the value of the expression.	Propiedad Asociativa	Una propiedad que establece que los números en expresiones de suma o de multiplicación pueden ser agrupados sin afectar el valor de la expresión.
Axes	A horizontal and vertical number line on a coordinate plane. 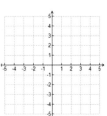	Ejes	Una recta numérica horizontal y vertical en un plano de coordenadas. 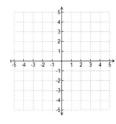

B

Bar Graph	A graph that uses bars to compare the quantities in a categorical data set. 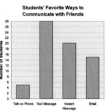	Gráfico de Barras	Una gráfica que utiliza barras para comparar las cantidades en un conjunto de datos categórico. 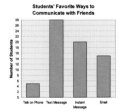
Base of a Power	The repeated factor in a power.	Base de un Potencia	El factor repetido en una potencia.
Base of a Solid	See Prism, Cylinder, Pyramid and Cone.	Base de un Sólido	Ver Prisma, Cilindro, Pirámide y Cono.
Base of a Triangle	Any side of a triangle.	Base de un Triángulo.	Cualquier lado de un Triángulo.
Bias	A problem when gathering data that affects the results of the data.	Sesgo	Un problema que ocurre cuando se recogen datos que afectan los resultados de los datos.

| Box-and-Whisker Plot | A diagram used to display the five-number summary of a data set. 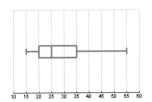 | Diagrama de Líneas y Bloques | Un diagrama utilizado para mostrar el resumen de cinco números de un conjunto de datos. 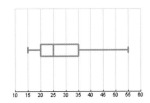 |

C

Categorical Data	Data collected in the form of words.	Datos Categóricos	Datos recopilados en la forma de palabras.
Center of a Circle	The point inside a circle that is the same distance from all points on the circle.	Centro de un Círculo	Un ángulo dentro de un círculo que está a la misma distancia de todos los puntos en el círculo.
Central Angle	An angle in a circle with its vertex at the center of the circle.	Ángulo Central	Un ángulo en un círculo con su vértice en el centro del círculo.
Chord	A line segment with endpoints on the circle.	Cuerda	Un segmento de la recta con puntos finales en el círculo.
Circle	The set of all points that are the same distance from a center point.	Círculo	El conjunto de todos los puntos que están a la misma distancia de un punto central.
Circumference	The distance around a circle.	Circunferencia	La distancia alrededor de un círculo.
Coefficient	The number multiplied by a variable in a term.	Coeficiente	El número multiplicado por una variable en un término.

English		Spanish	
Commutative Property	A property that states numbers can be added or multiplied in any order.	Propiedad Conmutativa	Una propiedad que establece que los números pueden ser sumados o multiplicados en cualquier orden.
Compatible Numbers	Numbers that are easy to mentally compute; used when estimating products and quotients.	Números Compatibles	Números que son fáciles de calcular mentalmente; utilizado cuando se estiman productos y cocientes.
Complementary Angles	Two angles whose sum is 90°.	Ángulos Complementarios	Dos ángulos cuya suma es de 90°.
Complements	Two probabilities whose sum is 1. Together they make up all the possible outcomes without repeating any outcomes.	Complementos	Dos probabilidades cuya suma es de 1. Juntos crean todos los posibles resultados sin repetir alguno.
Composite Figure	A geometric figure made of two or more geometric shapes.	Figura Compuesta	Una figura geométrica formada por dos o más formas geométricas.
Composite Number	A whole number larger than 1 that has more than two factors.	Número Compuesto	Un número entero mayor que el 1 con más de dos factores.
Composite Solid	A solid made of two or more three-dimensional geometric figures.	Sólido Compuesto	Un sólido formado por dos o más figuras geométricas tridimensionales.
Cone	A solid formed by one circular base and a vertex.	Cono	Un sólido formado por una base circular y una vértice.
Congruent	Equal in measure.	Congruente	Igual en medida.
Congruent Figures	Two shapes that have the exact same shape and the exact same size.	Figuras Congruentes	Dos figuras que tienen exactamente la misma forma y el mismo tamaño.
Constant	A term that has no variable.	Constante	Un término que no tiene variable.

Continuous	When a graph can be drawn from beginning to end without any breaks.	Continuo	Cuando una gráfica puede ser dibujada desde principio a fin sin ninguna interrupción.
Conversion	The process of renaming a measurement using different units.	Conversión	El proceso de renombrar una medida utilizando diferentes unidades.
Coordinate Plane	A plane created by two number lines intersecting at a 90º angle.	Plano de Coordenadas	Un plano creado por dos rectas numéricas que se intersecan a un ángulo de 90°.

Correlation	The relationship between two variables in a scatter plot.	Correlación	La relación entre dos variables en un gráfico de dispersión.
Corresponding Angles	Two non-adjacent angles that are on the same side of a transversal with one angle inside the two lines and the other on the outside of the two lines.	Ángulos Correspondientes	Dos ángulos no adyacentes que están en el mismo lado de una transversal con un ángulo adentro de las dos rectas y el otro afuera de las dos rectas.

Corresponding Parts	The angles and sides in similar or congruent figures that match.	Partes Correspondientes	Los ángulos y lados en figuras similares o congruentes que concuerdan.
Cubed	A number to the third power.	Elevado al Cubo	Un número elevado a la tercera potencia.
Cylinder	A solid formed by two congruent and parallel circular bases.	Cilindro	Un sólido formado por dos bases circulares congruentes y paralelas.

D

Decimal	A number with a digit in the tenths place, hundredths place, etc.	Decimal	Un número con un dígito en las décimas, las centenas, etc.
Degrees	A unit used to measure angles.	Grados	Una unidad utilizada para medir ángulos.
Descending Order	Numbers arranged from greatest to least.	Progresión Descendente	Los números ordenados de mayor a menor.
Diameter	The distance across a circle through the center.	Diámetro	La distancia a través de un círculo por el centro.

Direct Variation	A linear function that passes through the origin and has equation $y = mx$.	Variación Directa	Una función lineal que pasa a través del origen y tiene la ecuación $y = mx$.
Discount	The decrease in the price of an item.	Descuento	La disminución de precio en un artículo.
Discrete	When a graph can be represented by a unique set of points rather than a continuous line.	Discreto	Cuando una gráfica puede ser representada por un conjunto de puntos único en vez de una recta continua.
Distance Formula	A formula used to find the distance between two points on the coordinate plane. $d = \sqrt{(x_2 - x_1)^2 + (y_2 - y_1)^2}$	Fórmula de Distancia	Una fórmula utilizada para encontrar la distancia entre dos puntos en un plano de coordenadas. $d = \sqrt{(x_2 - x_1)^2 + (y_2 - y_1)^2}$
Distributive Property	A property that can be used to rewrite an expression without parentheses. $a(b + c) = ab + ac$	Propiedad Distributiva	Una propiedad que puede ser utilizada para reescribir una expresión sin paréntesis: $a(b + c) = ab + ac$
Dividend	The number being divided. Example: $100 \div 4 = 25$	Dividendo	El número que es dividido. Ejemplo: $100 \div 4 = 25$
Divisor	The number used to divide. Example: $100 \div 4 = 25$	Divisor	El número utilizado para dividir. Ejemplo: $100 \div 4 = 25$

| Double Stem-and-Leaf Plot | A stem-and-leaf plot where one set of data is placed on the right side of the stem and another is placed on the left of the stem. | Doble Gráfica de Tallo y Hoja | Una gráfica de tallo y hoja donde un conjunto de datos es colocado al lado derecho del tallo y el otro es colocado a la izquierda del tallo. |

Jon's Movies		Scott's Movies
7	195	
7 7 5 4 1 0	196	7 8
2	197	
4 4	198	4 5 8 8
4	199	1 3 4 7 9
1	200	2

Key: 195 | 7 = 1957 copyright date

Jon's Movies		Scott's Movies
7	195	
7 7 5 4 1 0	196	7 8
2	197	
4 4	198	4 5 8 8
1	199	1 3 4 7 9
1	200	2

Key: 195 | 7 = 1957 copyright date

E

| Edge | The segment where two faces of a solid meet. | Arista (Borde) | El segmento donde dos caras de un sólido se encuentran. |

edge

arista

| Elimination Method | A method for solving a system of linear equations. | Método de Eliminación | Un método para resolver un sistema de ecuaciones lineales. |

| Equally Likely | Two or more possible outcomes of a given situation that have the same probability. | Igualmente Probables | Dos o más posibles resultados de una situación dada que tienen la misma probabilidad. |

| Equation | A mathematical sentence that contains an equals sign between 2 expressions. | Ecuación | Una oración matemática que contiene un símbolo de igualdad entre dos expresiones. |

| Equiangular | A polygon in which all angles are congruent. | Equiángulo | Un polígono en el cual todos los ángulos son congruentes. |

| Equilateral | A polygon in which all sides are congruent. | Equilátero | Un polígono en el cual todos los lados son congruentes. |

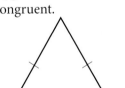

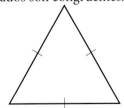

| Equivalent Decimals | Two or more decimals that represent the same number. | Decimales Equivalentes | Dos o más decimales que representan el mismo número. |

| Equivalent Expressions | Two or more expressions that represent the same algebraic expression. | Expresiones Equivalentes | Dos o más expresiones que representan la misma expresión algebraica. |

Equivalent Fractions	Two or more fractions that represent the same number.	Fracciones Equivalentes	Dos o más fracciones que representan el mismo número.
Evaluate	To find the value of an expression.	Evaluar	Encontrar el valor de una expresión.
Even Distribution	A set of data values that is evenly spread across the range of the data.	Distribución Igualada	Un conjunto de valores de datos que es esparcido de modo uniforme a través de la extensión de los datos.
Event	A desired outcome or group of outcomes.	Suceso	Un resultado o grupo de resultados deseados.
Experimental Probability	The ratio of the number of times an event occurs to the total number of trials.	Probabilidad Experimental	La razón de la cantidad de veces que un suceso ocurre a la cantidad total de intentos.
Exponent	The number of times a factor is repeated in a power.	Exponente	La cantidad de veces que un factor es repetido en una potencia.

F

Face	A polygon that is a side or base of a solid.	Cara	Un polígono que es una base de lado de un sólido.

face

cara

Factors	Whole numbers that can be multiplied together to find a product.	Factores	Números enteros que pueden ser multiplicados entre si para encontrar un producto.
First Quartile (Q1)	The median of the lower half of a data set.	Primer Cuartil (Q1)	Mediana de la parte inferior de un conjunto de datos.
Five-Number Summary	Describes the spread of a data set using the minimum, 1st quartile, median, 3rd quartile and maximum.	Resumen de Cinco Números	Describe la extensión de un conjunto de datos utilizando el mínimo, el primer cuartil, la mediana el tercer cuartil y el máximo.
Formula	An algebraic equation that shows the relationship among specific quantities.	Fórmula	Una ecuación algebraica que enseña la relación entre cantidades específicas.
Fraction	A number that represents a part of a whole number, written as $\frac{numerator}{denominator}$.	Fracción	Un número que representa una parte de un número entero, escrito como $\frac{numerador}{denominador}$.

| Frequency | The number of times an item occurs in a data set. | Frecuencia | La cantidad de veces que un artículo ocurre en un conjunto de datos. |

| Frequency Table | A table which shows how many times a value occurs in a given interval. | Tabla de Frecuencia | Una tabla que enseña cuantas veces un valor ocurre en un intervalo dado. |

Weight of Newborn (in Pounds)	Tally
4 – 5.5	I
5.5 – 7	III
7 – 8.5	IIII
8.5 – 10	II
10 – 11.5	I

Weight of Newborn (in Pounds)	Tally
4 – 5.5	I
5.5 – 7	III
7 – 8.5	IIII
8.5 – 10	II
10 – 11.5	I

| Function | A pairing of input and output values according to a specific rule. | Función | El emparejamiento de valores de entrada y salida de acuerdo a una regla específica. |

G

| Geometric Probability | Ratios of lengths or areas used to find the likelihood of an event. | Probabilidad Geométrica | Razones de longitudes o áreas utilizadas para encontrar la probabilidad de un suceso. |

| Geometric Sequence | A list of numbers created by multiplying the previous term in the sequence by a common ratio. | Secuencia Geométrica | Una lista de números creada al multiplicar el término anterior en la secuencia por una razón común. |

| Greatest Common Factor (GCF) | The greatest factor that is common to two or more numbers. | Máximo Común Divisor (MCD) | El máximo divisor que le es común a dos o más números. |

| Grouping Symbols | Symbols such as parentheses or fraction bars that group parts of an expression. | Símbolos de Agrupación | Símbolos como el paréntesis o barras de fracción que agrupan las partes de una expresión. |

H

| Height of a Triangle | A perpendicular line drawn from the side whose length is the base to the opposite vertex. | Altura de un Triángulo | Una recta perpendicular dibujada desde el lado cuya longitud es la base al vértice opuesto. |

Histogram	A bar graph that displays the frequency of numerical data in equal-sized intervals.	Histograma	Un gráfico de barras que muestra la frecuencia de datos numéricos en intervalos de tamaños iguales.

Hypotenuse	The side opposite the right angle in a right triangle.	Hipotenusa	El lado opuesto el ángulo recto en un triángulo rectángulo.

I-J-K

Improper Fraction	A fraction whose numerator is greater than or equal to its denominator.	Fracción Impropia	Una fracción cuyo numerador es mayor o igual a su denominador.
Input-Output Table	A table used to describe a function by listing input values with their output values.	Tabla de Entrada y Salida	Una tabla utilizada para describir una función al enumerar valores de entrada con sus valores de salidas.

Input, x	Output, y

Input, x	Output, y

Integers	The set of all whole numbers, their opposites, and 0.	Enteros	El conjunto de todos los números enteros, sus opuestos y 0.
Interquartile Range (IQR)	The difference between the 3rd quartile and the 1st quartile in a set of data.	Rango Intercuartil (IQR)	La diferencia entre el tercer cuartil y el primer cuartil en un conjunto de datos.
Inverse Operations	Operations that undo each other.	Operaciones Inversas	Operaciones que se cancelan la una a la otra.
IQR Method	A method for determining outliers.	Método IQR	Un método para determinar los datos aberrantes.
Irrational Numbers	A number that cannot be expressed as a fraction of two integers.	Números Irracionales	Un número que no puede ser expresado como una fracción de dos enteros.

Isosceles Trapezoid	A trapezoid that has congruent legs. 	Trapezoide Isósceles	Un trapezoide con catetos congruentes. 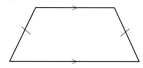
Isosceles Triangle	A triangle that has two or more congruent sides.	Triángulo Isósceles	Un triángulo que tiene dos o más lados congruentes.

L

Lateral Face	A side of a solid that is not a base.	Cara Lateral	Un lado de un sólido que no sea una base.
Least Common Denominator (LCD)	The least common multiple of two or more denominators.	Mínimo Común Denominador (MCD)	El mínimo común múltiplo de dos o más denominadores.
Least Common Multiple (LCM)	The smallest nonzero multiple that is common to two or more numbers.	Mínimo Común Múltiplo (MCM)	El múltiplo más pequeño que no sea cero que le es común a dos o más números.
Leg	The two sides of a right triangle that form a right angle. 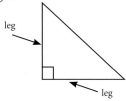	Cateto	Los dos lados de un triángulo rectángulo que forman un ángulo recto. 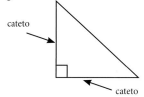
Like Terms	Terms that have the same variable(s).	Términos Semejantes	Términos que tienen el mismo variable(s).
Line of Best Fit	A line which best represents the pattern of a two-variable data set. 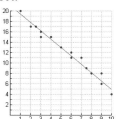	Recta de Mejor Ajuste	Una recta que mejor representa el patrón de un conjunto de datos de dos variables. 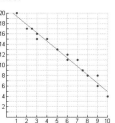

Linear Equation	An equation whose graph is a line.	Ecuación Lineal	Una ecuación cuya gráfica es una recta.
Linear Function	A function whose graph is a line.	Función Lineal	Una función cuya gráfica es una recta.
Linear Pair	Two adjacent angles whose non-common sides are opposite rays.	Par Lineal	Dos ángulos adyacentes cuyos lados no comunes son rayos opuestos.

M

Markup	The increase in the price of an item.	Margen de Beneficio	El aumento de precio en un artículo.
Mean	The sum of all values in a data set divided by the number of values.	Media	La suma de todos los valores en un conjunto de datos dividido entre la cantidad de valores.
Measures of Center	Numbers that are used to represent a data set with a single value; the mean, median, and mode are the measures of center.	Medidas de Centro	Números que son utilizados para representar un conjunto de datos con un solo valor; la media, la mediana, y la moda son las medidas de centro.
Median	The middle number or the average of the two middle numbers in an ordered data set.	Mediana	El número medio o el promedio de los dos números medios en un conjunto de datos ordenados.
Mixed Number	The sum of a whole number and a fraction less than 1.	Números Mixtos	La suma de un número entero y una fracción menor que 1.
Mode	The number(s) or item(s) that occur most often in a data set.	Moda	El número(s) o artículo(s) que ocurre con más frecuencia en un conjunto de datos.
Motion Rate	A rate that compares distance to time.	Índice de Movimiento	Un índice que compara distancia por tiempo.
Multiple	The product of a number and nonzero whole number.	Múltiplo	El producto de un número y un número entero que no sea cero.

N

| Negative Number | A number less than 0. | Número Negativo | Un número menor que 0. |

| Net | A two-dimensional pattern that folds to form a solid. | Red | Un patrón bidimensional que se dobla para formar un sólido. |

| Non-Linear Function | A function whose graph does not form a line. | Ecuación No Lineal | Una ecuación cuya gráfica no forma una recta. |

| Normal Distribution | A set of data values where the majority of the values are located in the middle of the data set and can be displayed by a bell-shaped curve. | Distribución Normal | Un conjunto de valores de datos donde la mayoría de los valores están localizados en el medio del conjunto de datos y pueden ser mostrados por una curva de forma de campana. |

| Numerical Data | Data collected in the form of numbers. | Datos Numéricos | Datos recopilados en la forma de números. |

| Numerical Expressions | An expression consisting of numbers and operations that represents a specific value. | Expresiones Numéricas | Una expresión que consta de números y operaciones que representa un valor específico. |

O

| Obtuse Angle | An angle that measures more than 90° but less than 180°. | Ángulo Obtuso | Un ángulo que mide más de 90° pero menos de 180°. |

| Opposites | Numbers the same distance from 0 on a number line but are on opposite sides of 0. | Opuestos | Números a la misma distancia del 0 en un recta numérica pero en lados opuestos del 0. |

| Order of Operations | The rules to follow when evaluating an expression with more than one operation. | Orden de las Operaciones | Las reglas a seguir cuando se evalúa una expresión con más de una operación. |

| Ordered Pair | A pair of numbers used to locate a point on a coordinate plane (x, y). | Pares Ordenados | Un par de números utilizados para localizar un punto en un plano de coordenadas (x, y). |

Origin	The point where the x- and y-axis intersect on a coordinate plane $(0, 0)$.	Origen	El punto donde el eje de la x- y el de la y- se cruzan en un plano de coordinadas $(0,0)$.

Outcome	One possible result from an experiment or probability event.	Resultado	Un resultado posible de un experimento o un suceso de probabilidad.
Outlier	An extreme value that varies greatly from the other values in a data set.	Dato Aberrante	Un valor extremo que varía mucho de los otros valores en un conjunto de datos.

P

Parallel	Lines in the same plane that never intersect.	Paralela	Rectas en el mismo plano que nunca se intersecan.
Parallel Box-and-Whisker Plot	One box-and-whisker plot placed above another used to compare data sets.	Diagrama Paralelo de Líneas y Bloques	Un diagrama de líneas y bloques ubicado sobre otro para comparar conjuntos de datos.
Parallelogram	A quadrilateral with both pairs of opposite sides parallel.	Paralelogramo	Un cuadrilateral con ambos pares de lados opuestos paralelos.
Parent Graph	The most basic graph of a function.	Gráfico Matriz	La gráfica más básica de una función.
Percent	A ratio that compares a number to 100.	Por ciento	Una razón que compara un número con 100.
Percent of Change	The percent a quantity increases or decreases compared to the original amount.	Por ciento de Cambio	El por ciento que una cantidad aumenta o disminuye comparado a la cantidad original.

Percent of Decrease	The percent of change when the new amount is less than the original amount.	Por ciento de Disminución	El por ciento de cambio cuando la nueva cantidad es menos que la cantidad original.
Percent of Increase	The percent of change when the new amount is more than the original amount.	Por ciento de Incremento	El por ciento de cambio cuando la nueva cantidad es más que la cantidad original.
Perfect Square	A number whose square root is an integer.	Cuadrado Perfecto	Un número cuya raíz cuadrada es un entero.
Perimeter	The distance around a figure.	Perímetro	La distancia alrededor de una figura.
Perpendicular	Two lines or segments that form a right angle.	Perpendicular	Dos rectas o segmentos que forman un ángulo recto.
Pi (π)	The ratio of the circumference of a circle to its diameter.	Pi (π)	La razón de la circunferencia de un círculo a su diámetro.
Pictograph	A graph that uses pictures to compare the amounts represented in a categorical data set.	Gráfica Pictórica	Una gráfica que utiliza dibujos para comparar las cantidades representadas en un conjunto de datos categóricos.
Pie Chart	A circle graph that shows information as sectors of a circle.	Gráfico Circular	Enseña la información como sectores de un círculo.
Polygon	A closed figure formed by three or more line segments.	Polígono	Una figura cerrada formada por tres o más segmentos de rectas.

Positive Number	A number greater than 0.	Número Positivo	Un número mayor que 0.
Power	An expression using an exponent that represents the product of a repeated factor.	Potencia	Una expresión que utiliza un exponente que representa el producto de un factor repetido.
Prime Factorization	When any composite number is written as the product of all its prime factors.	Factorización Prima	Cuando cualquier número compuesto es escrito como el producto de todos los factores primos.
Prime Number	A whole number larger than 1 that has only two possible factors, 1 and itself.	Número Primo	Un número entero mayor que 1 que tiene solo dos factores posibles, 1 y el mismo.
Prism	A solid formed by polygons with two congruent, parallel bases.	Prisma	Un sólido formado por polígonos con dos bases congruentes y paralelas.
Probability	The measure of how likely it is an event will occur.	Probabilidad	La medida de cuán probable un suceso puede ocurrir.
Proper Fraction	A fraction with a numerator that is less than the denominator.	Fracción Propia	Una fracción con un numerador que es menos que el denominador.
Proportion	An equation stating two ratios are equivalent.	Proporción	Una ecuación que establece que dos razones son equivalentes.
Protractor	A tool used to measure angles.	Transportador	Una herramienta para medir ángulos.
Pyramid	A solid with a polygonal base and triangular sides that meet at a vertex.	Pirámide	Un sólido con una base poligonal y lados triangulares que se encuentran en un vértice.

Pythagorean Triple	A set of three positive integers (a, b, c) such that $a^2 + b^2 = c^2$.	Triple de Pitágoras	Un conjunto de tres enteros positivos (a, b, c) tal que $a^2 + b^2 = c^2$.

Q

Q-Points	Points that are created by the intersection of the quartiles for the x- and y-values of a two-variable data set.	Puntos Q	Puntos que son creados por la intersección de los cuartiles para los valores de la x- y la y- de un conjunto de datos de dos variables.
Quadrants	Four regions formed by the x and y axes on a coordinate plane.	Cuadrantes	Cuatro regiones formadas por el eje-x y el eje-y en un plano de coordenadas.
Quadrilateral	A polygon with four sides.	Cuadrilateral	Un polígono con cuatro lados.
Quotient	The answer to a division problem.	Cociente	La solución a un problema de división.

R

Radius	The distance from the center of a circle to any point on the circle.	Radio	La distancia desde el centro de un círculo a cualquier punto en el círculo.
Random Sample	A sample that is representative of the population being studied, with each person or object having an equal chance of being included.	Muestra Aleatoria	Una muestra que representa a la población que es estudiada; cada persona o objeto tiene la misma oportunidad de ser incluido.
Range	The difference between the maximum and minimum values in a data set.	Extensión	La diferencia entre los valores máximo y mínimo en un conjunto de datos.
Rate	A ratio of two numbers that have different units.	Índice	Una proporción de dos números con diferentes unidades.

Rate Conversion	A process of changing at least one unit of measurement in a rate to a different unit of measurement.	Conversión de Índice	Un proceso de cambiar por lo menos una unidad de medición en un índice a una diferente unidad de medición.
Rate of Change	The change in y-values over the change in x-values on a linear graph.	Índice de Cambio	El cambio en los valores de y sobre el cambio en los valores de x en una gráfica lineal.
Ratio	A comparison of two numbers using division. $a:b$ $\dfrac{a}{b}$ a to b	Razón	Una comparación de dos números utilizando división. $a:b$ $\dfrac{a}{b}$ a to b
Rational Number	A number that can be expressed as a fraction of two integers.	Número Racional	Un número que puede ser expresado como una fracción de dos enteros.
Ray	A part of a line that has one endpoint and extends forever in one direction.	Rayo	Una parte de una recta que tiene un punto final y se extiende eternamente en una dirección.
Real Numbers	The set of numbers that includes all rational and irrational numbers.	Números Racionales	El conjunto de números que incluye todos los números racionales e irracionales.
Reciprocals	Two numbers whose product is 1.	Recíprocos	Dos números cuyo producto es 1.
Recursive Routine	A routine described by stating the start value and the operation performed to get the following terms.	Rutina Recursiva	Una rutina descrita al exponer el valor del comienzo y la operación realizada para conseguir los términos siguientes.
Recursive Sequence	An ordered list of numbers created by a first term and a repeated operation.	Secuencia Recursiva	Una lista de números ordenados creada por un primer término y una operación repetida.
Repeating Decimal	A decimal that has one or more digits that repeat forever.	Decimal Repetitivo	Un decimal que tiene uno o más dígitos que se repiten eternamente.
Right Angle	An angle that measures 90°.	Ángulo Recto	Un ángulo que mide 90°.

Sales Tax	An amount added to the cost of an item. The amount added is a percent of the original amount as determined by a state, county or city.	Impuesto sobre las Ventas	Una cantidad añadida al costo de un artículo. La cantidad añadida es un por ciento de la cantidad original determinado por el estado, condado o ciudad.
Same-Side Interior Angles	Two angles that are on the inside of two lines and are on the same side of a transversal.	Ángulos Interiores del Mismo Lado	Dos ángulos que están en el interior de dos rectas y están en el mismo lado de una transversal.
Sample	A part of the population that is used to make conclusions about the entire population.	Muestra	Una parte de la población que es utilizada para formular conclusiones de la población entera.
Sample Space	The set of all possible outcomes for an event.	Muestra de Espacio	El conjunto de todos los posibles resultados para un suceso.
Scale	The ratio of a length on a map or model to the actual object.	Escala	La razón de una longitud en un mapa o modelo al objeto verdadero.
Scale Factor	The ratio of corresponding sides in two similar figures.	Factor de Escala	La razón de los lados correspondientes en dos figuras similares.
Scalene Triangle	A triangle that has no congruent sides.	Triángulo Escaleno	Un triángulo sin lados congruentes.
Scatter Plot	A set of ordered pairs graphed on a coordinate plane.	Diagrama de Dispersión	Un conjunto de pares ordenados graficados en un plano de coordenadas.

| Scientific Notation | A way of writing extremely large or small numbers as the product of a number between 1 and 10 and a power of 10. | Notación Científica | Una manera de escribir números extremadamente grandes o pequeños como el producto de un número entre 1 y 10 y una potencia de 10. |

Sector — A portion of a circle enclosed by two radii.

Sector — Una porción de un circulo encerado por dos radios.

Sequence — An ordered list of numbers.

Sucesión — Una lista de números ordenados.

Similar Figures — Two figures that have the exact same shape, but not necessarily the exact same size.

Figuras Similares — Dos figuras que tienen exactamente la misma forma, pero no necesariamente el mismo tamaño exacto.

Similar Solids — Solids that have the same shape and all corresponding dimensions are proportional.

Sólidos Similares — Sólidos con la misma forma y todas sus dimensiones correspondientes son proporcionales.

Simplest Form — A fraction whose numerator and denominator's only common factor is 1.

Expresión Mínima — Una fracción cuyo único factor común del numerador y del denominador es 1.

Simplify an Expression — To rewrite an expression without parentheses and combine all like terms.

Simplificar una Expresión — Reescribir una expresión sin paréntesis y combinar todos los términos iguales.

Single-Variable Data — A data set with only one type of data.

Datos de una Variable — Un conjunto de datos con tan solo un tipo de datos.

Sketch — To make a figure free hand without the use of measurement tools.

Esbozo — Hacer una figura a mano libre sin utilizar herramientas de medidas.

Skewed Left	A plot or graph with a longer tail on the left-hand side.	Torcido a la Izquierda	Un gráfico con una cola al lado izquierdo.
Skewed Right	A plot or graph with a longer tail on the right-hand side.	Torcido a la Derecha	Un gráfico con una cola al lado derecho.
Slant Height	The height of a lateral face of a pyramid or cone.	Altura Sesgada	La altura de un cara lateral de una pirámide o cono.

Slope	The ratio of the vertical change to the horizontal change in a linear graph.	Pendiente	La razón del cambio vertical al cambio horizontal en una gráfica lineal.
Slope Triangle	A right triangle formed where one leg represents the vertical rise and the other leg is the horizontal run in a linear graph.	Triángulo de Pendiente	Un triángulo rectángulo formado donde una cateto representa el ascenso y la otra es una carrera horizontal en una gráfica lineal.

Slope-Intercept Form	A linear equation written in the form $y = mx + b$.	Forma de las Intersecciones con la Pendiente	Una ecuación lineal escrita en la forma $y = mx + b$.
Solid	A three-dimensional figure that encloses a part of space.	Sólido	Una figura tridimensional que encierra una parte del espacio.
Solution	Any value or values that makes an equation true.	Solución	Cualquier valor o valores que hacen una ecuación verdadera.
Solution of a System of Linear Equations	The ordered pair that satisfies both linear equations in the system.	Solución de un Sistema de Ecuaciones Lineales	El par ordenado que satisface ambas ecuaciones lineales en el sistema.

Sphere	A solid formed by a set of points in space that are the same distance from a center point.	Esfera	Un sólido formado por un conjunto de puntos en el espacio que están a la misma distancia de un punto central.

Square Root	One of the two equal factors of a number. $25 = 5 \cdot 5 \qquad \sqrt{25} = 5$	Raíz Cuadrada	Uno de los factores iguales de un número. $25 = 5 \cdot 5 \qquad \sqrt{25} = 5$
Squared	A number to the second power.	al Cuadrado	Un número a la segunda potencia.
Start Value	The output value that is paired with an input value of 0 in an input-output table.	Valor de Comienzo	El valor de salida que es aparejado con un valor de entrada de 0 en una tabla de entradas y salidas.
Statistics	The process of collecting, displaying and analyzing a set of data.	Estadísticas	El proceso de recopilar, exponer y analizar un conjunto de datos.
Stem-and-Leaf Plot	A plot which uses the digits of the data values to show the shape and distribution of the data set.	Gráfica de Tallo y Hoja	Un diagrama que utiliza los dígitos de los valores de datos para mostrar la forma y la distribución del conjunto de datos.

```
 5 | 6
 6 |
 7 | 2  5  9  9
 8 | 0  0  6  8  9
 9 | 2  3  4  8
10 | 0  0
Key: 7 | 5 = 75
```

```
 5 | 6
 6 |
 7 | 2  5  9  9
 8 | 0  0  6  8  9
 9 | 2  3  4  8
10 | 0  0
Key: 7 | 5 = 75
```

Straight Angle	An angle that measures 180°.	Ángulo Llano	Un ángulo que mide 180°.
Substitution Method	A method for solving a system of linear equations.	Método de Substitución	Un método para resolver un sistema de ecuaciones lineales.
Supplementary Angles	Two angles whose sum is 180°.	Ángulos Suplementarios	Dos ángulos cuya suma es 180°.
Surface Area	The sum of the areas of all the surfaces on a solid.	Área de la Superficie	La suma de las áreas de todas las superficies en un sólido.
System of Linear Equations	Two or more linear equations.	Sistema de Ecuaciones Lineales	Dos o más ecuaciones lineales.

T

Term	A number or the product of a number and a variable in an algebraic expression; A number in a sequence.	Término	Un número o el producto de un número y una variable en una expresión algebraica; Un número en una sucesión.
Terminating Decimal	A decimal that stops.	Decimal Finito	Un decimal que para.
Theorem	A relationship in mathematics that has been proven.	Teorema	Una relación en las matemáticas que ha sido probada.
Theoretical Probability	The ratio of favorable outcomes to the number of possible outcomes.	Probabilidad Teórica	La proporción de resultados favorables a la cantidad de resultados posibles.
Third Quartile (Q3)	The median of the upper half of a data set.	Tercer Cuartil (Q3)	Mediana de la parte superior de un conjunto de datos.
Tick Marks	Equally divided spaces marked with a small line between every inch or centimeter on a ruler.	Marcas de Graduación	Espacios divididos igualmente marcados con una línea pequeña entre cada pulgada o centímetro en una regla.
Transversal	A line that intersects two or more lines in the same plane.	Transversal	Una recta que interseca dos o más rectas en el mismo plano.
Trapezoid	A quadrilateral with exactly one pair of parallel sides.	Trapezoide	Un cuadrilateral con exactamente un par de lados paralelos.
Trial	A single act of performing an experiment.	Prueba	Un solo intento de realizar un experimento.
Two-Step Equation	An equation that has two different operations.	Ecuación de Dos Pasos	Una ecuación que tiene dos operaciones diferentes.
Two-Variable Data	A data set where two groups of numbers are looked at simultaneously.	Datos de dos Variables	Un conjunto de datos dónde dos grupos de números se observan simultáneamente.

U-V-W-X-Y-Z

English	Definition	Spanish	Definición
Unit Rate	A rate with a denominator of 1.	Índice de Unidad	Un índice con un denominador de 1.
Variable	A symbol that represents one or more numbers.	Variable	Un símbolo que representa uno o más números.
Vertex of a Solid	The point where three or more edges meet. 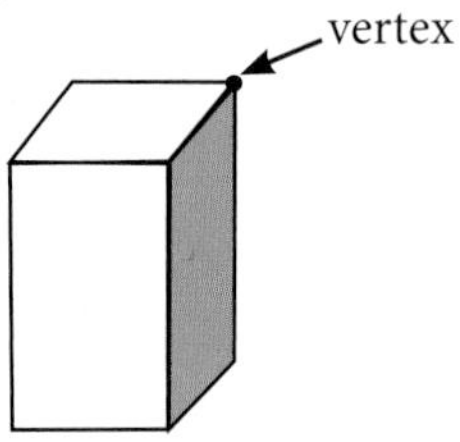	Vértice de un Sólido	El punto donde tres o más bordes se encuentran. 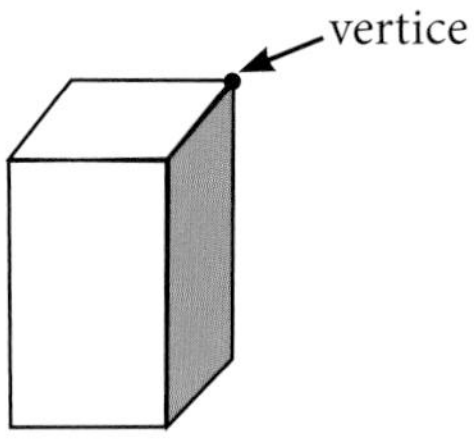

vertex

vertice

Vertex of a Triangle	A point where two sides of a triangle meet. 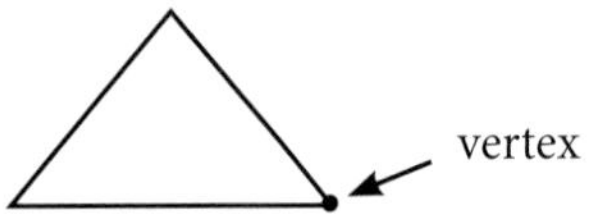	Vértice de un Triángulo	Un punto donde dos lados de un triángulo se encuentran. 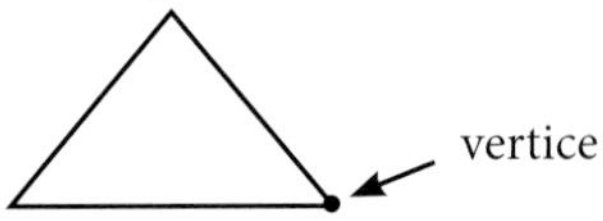

vertex

vertice

Vertex of an Angle	The common endpoint of the two rays that form an angle. 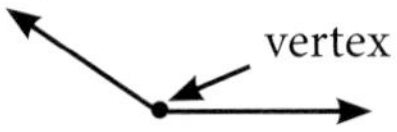	Vértice de un Ángulo	El punto final en común de los dos rayos que forma un ángulo. 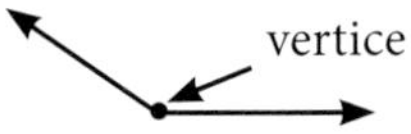

vertex

vertice

Vertical Angles	Non-adjacent angles with a common vertex formed by two intersecting lines. 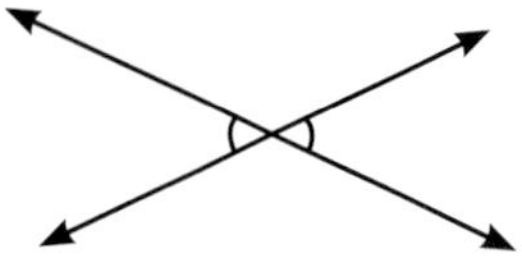	Ángulos Verticales	Ángulos no adyacentes con un vértice en común formado por dos rectas intersecantes. 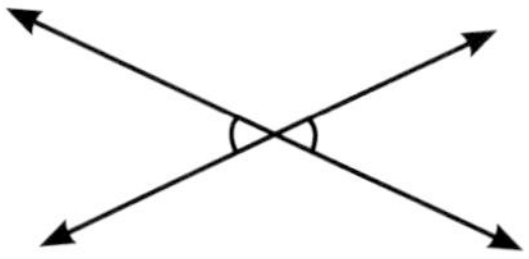
Volume	The number of cubic units needed to fill a solid.	Volumen	La cantidad de unidades cúbicas necesitadas para llenar un sólido.
x-Axis	The horizontal number line on a coordinate plane. 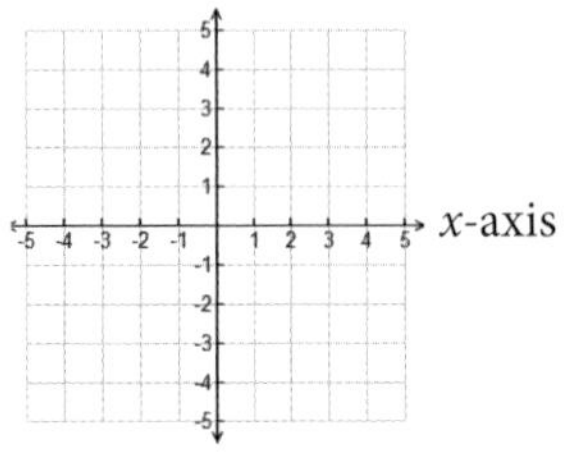	Eje-x, Eje de la x	La recta numérica horizontal en un plano de coordenadas. 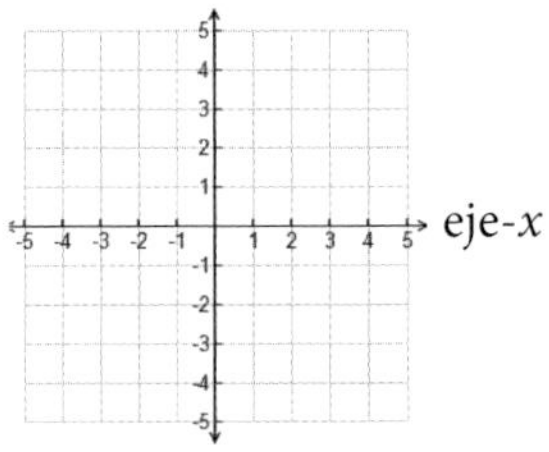

x-axis

eje-x

y-Axis	The vertical number line on a coordinate plane.	Eje-*y*, Eje de la *y*	La recta numérica vertical en un plano de coordenadas.

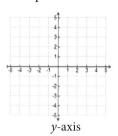

y-axis

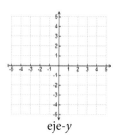

eje-*y*

y-Intercept	The point where a graph intersects the *y*-axis.	Intersección *y*	El punto donde una gráfica interseca el eje-*y*.

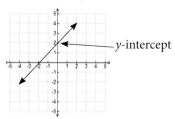

y-intercept

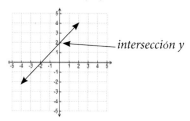

intersección y

Zero Pair	One positive integer chip paired with one negative integer chip.	Par Cero	Un chip entero positivo emparejado con un chip entero negativo.

$$\bullet \; + \; \bullet \; = \; 0$$

$$1 \; + \; (-1) \; = \; 0$$

$$\bullet \; + \; \bullet \; = \; 0$$

$$1 \; + \; (-1) \; = \; 0$$

SELECTED ANSWERS

BLOCK 1

Lesson 1

1. a) Nathan: multiplication **b)** Subtraction **3.** 28 **5.** 17 **7.** 21
9. 4 **11.** 8 **13.** 5 **15.** −12 **17. a)** $130 \cdot 5 + 40 \cdot 8$ **b)** $970
19. Answers may vary **21.** $(6 + 3 + 11) \div 4 = 5$
23. $-1 \cdot 6 + 8 - 4 \div (2 + 2) = 1$

Lesson 2

1. 5 **3.** −6 **5.** 22 **7.** 8 **9.** 30 **11.** 1 **13.** 1

15.

x	$6x - 4$	Output
−2	$6(-2) - 4$	−16
0	$6(0) - 4$	−4
$\frac{1}{2}$	$6\left(\frac{1}{2}\right) - 4$	−1
3	$6(3) - 4$	14
8	$6(8) - 4$	44

17. True **19.** False

21. True **23.** False **25. a)** 18 units **b)** 26 units **c)** 22 units
27. a) $12x + 16y$ **b)** $116 **c)** Answers may vary **29.** −1
31. −2 **33.** −53

Lesson 3

1. $5x + 5$ **3.** $8m + 10$ **5.** $-3h + 33$ **7.** 735 **9.** 3,584
11. a) $7(15 - 0.05)$ **b)** $104.65 **13.** $13x - 8$ **15.** $-x + y$
17. $11y + 7x$ **19.** $6x + 1$ **21.** $5x + 10$ **23.** $10x - 8$ **25.** $6x + 18$
27. $44x - 77$ **29.** A. and C. $3x + 9$ **31. a)** 50 **b)** $\frac{4}{6} = \frac{2}{3}$ **c)** 53
d) 32

Lesson 4

1. $x = 31$ **3.** $x = 9$ **5.** $x = 61$ **7.** $x = -72$ **9.** $x = 22$
11. See student work; $x = 4$ **13.** $x + (-53) = 89$; $x = 142$
15. $x - 16 = 102$; $x = 118$ **17.** $\frac{1}{3} \cdot x = 6$; $x = 18$ **19. a)** $7x$
b) $7x = 84$; $x = 12$ **21.** $x = -160$ **23.** $x = \frac{7}{4}$ or $1\frac{3}{4}$ **25.** $x = -3.4$
27. 26 **29.** −6 **31.** $-18x + 2$ **33.** $2x - 1$

Lesson 5

1. $x = 4$ **3.** $x = 50$ **5.** $x = 11$ **7.** $x = -60$ **9.** $x = 10$
11. a) Subtracted instead of adding 6, $x = 11$ **b)** subtracted
from wrong side of equation, $x = 3$ **c)** divided by 8 instead of
multiplying, $x = 192$ **13.** $\frac{x}{3} - 6 = -1$; $x = 15$
15. $\frac{1}{2}x + 4 = 3$; $x = -2$ **17.** 8.5 hours **19.** $2 + 3 \times 5 = 17$
21. $-1 \times 2 + 2 = 0$ **23.** $9x - 18$ **25.** $10x$ **27.** $4x + 20$

Lesson 6

1. See student work; subtract x from both sides, then subtract
1 from both sides, then divide both sides by 2; $x = 4$ **3.** $x = 11$
5. $x = 1$ **7.** $x = 15$ **9. a)** $12 + 0.25x = 0.75x$ **b)** $x = 24$
c) $80 **11.** $x = 8$ **13.** $x = 5$ **15.** $x = 3$ **17.** $x = 4$ **19.** He forgot
to distribute the 3 and the 7. $x = -5$ **21.** True **23.** False

Lesson 7

1.

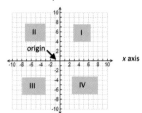

3. F = (−4,0); G = (7,3); H = (0,0); I = (2,−8); J = (0,5);
K = (−9,4) **5.** y-axis **7.** x-axis **9. a)**
b) Grade appears to go down as
the number of missing
assignments goes up.

11. a)

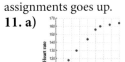

b) Goes up quickly, then levels off
c) answers may vary; around 170
13. $x = 5$ **15.** $x = 11$ **17.** $x = 22.2$
19. $x = 2$

Block 1 Review

1. 18 **3.** 11 **5.** 2 **7.** −11 **9.** 11 **11.** 8.4 **13.** −20 **15.** $\frac{9}{2}$ or $4\frac{1}{2}$

17.

x	$\frac{3x + 2}{4}$	Output
−3	$\frac{3(-3) + 2}{4}$	$-\frac{7}{4}$ or $-1\frac{3}{4}$
0	$\frac{3(0) + 2}{4}$	$\frac{1}{2}$
4	$\frac{3(4) + 2}{4}$	$\frac{7}{2}$ or $3\frac{1}{2}$
10	$\frac{3(10) + 2}{4}$	8

19. $2x - \frac{1}{2}$ **21.** $18x - 60$

23. $1.5x + 0.5$ **25.** $3x - 6$ **27.** $5x - 10$ **29.** $10x + 25$
31. $5(x - 4) = 5x - 20$ **33.** $x = -21$ **35.** $x = 5.5$ **37.** $x = 22.2$
39. $x - 10 = 66$; $x = 76$ **41.** $x = 10$ **43.** $x = 36$ **45.** $x = 5.5$
47. a) $72 **b)** $30 + 14m = S$ **c)** $m = 10$ **49.** $x = -2$ **51.** $x = 11$
53. $x = -1$ **55. a)** $400 - 20x$ **b)** $100 + 30x$
c) $400 - 20x = 100 + 30x$; $x = 6$ **57.** (−1,4) **59.** (−3,−1)
61. Answers may vary **63.** Answers may vary

BLOCK 2

Lesson 8

1. 3, 5, <u>7</u>, 9, <u>11</u>, <u>13</u>; SV: 3; Op: +2 **3.** 27, 22, 17, <u>12</u>, <u>7</u>, <u>2</u>; SV: 27; Op: −5 **5.** 23, <u>34</u>, 45, 56, <u>67</u>, <u>78</u>; SV: 23; Op: + 11 **7.** <u>2.3</u>, 2.7, 3.1, <u>3.5</u>, 3.9, <u>4.3</u>; SV: 2.3; Op: +0.4

9. a)

Minutes Spent Downhill Skiing	Total Daily Calories Burned
0	1,230
1	
2	
3	
4	

b) 6

c)

Minutes Spent Downhill Skiing	Total Daily Calories Burned
0	1,230
1	1,236
2	1,242
3	1,248
4	1,254

d) 1,470 calories

11. SV: 8; Op: +8; 72 **13.** SV: 9; Op: −4; −23

15. a) 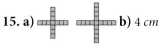 **b)** 4 *cm*

c) 12 *cm*; 20 *cm* **d)** SV: 4 Op: + 8 **e)** 52 *cm*

19.

x	$3(x-1)$	Output
−3	$3(-3-1)$	−12
0	$3(0-1)$	−3
2.2	$3(2.2-1)$	3.6
8	$3(8-1)$	21
21	$3(21-1)$	60

Lesson 9

1. SV: 10; Op: −2

x	y
0	10
1	8
2	6
3	4
4	2
5	0

3. SV: 2; Op: +0.5

x	y
0	2
1	2.5
2	3
3	3.5
4	4
5	4.5

5. SV: −1; Op: +2

x	y
0	−1
1	1
2	3
3	5
4	7
5	9

7. SV: 3 Op: None

x	y
0	3
1	3
2	3
3	3
4	3
5	3

9. a)

Time (seconds), x	Feet off the Ground, y
0	60
1	50
2	40
3	30
4	20
5	10
6	0

b) SV: 60; Op: −10

c) How tall the slide is **d)** 6 seconds **11.**
13. $6(2x − 3) = 12x − 18$
15. $\frac{1}{2} \cdot 2 (−3x + 26) = −3x + 26$

Lesson 10

1. Answers may vary **3.** Answers may vary
5. a) SV: 799 Op: −70 **b)**

Years Passed	Value of Maggie's Laptop
0	$799
1	$729
2	$659
3	$589
4	$519
5	$449

c) [graph: Value of the laptop vs Years passed] **d)** 12 years

7. a) SV: −61 Op: + 7 **b)**

Minutes Hiking	Elevation
0	−61
1	−54
2	−47
3	−40
4	−33
5	−26
6	−19
7	−12
8	−5
9	2
10	9

c) [graph: Elevation vs Minutes] **d)** Approximately 9 minutes

9. a) SV: $1,000 Op: +$250 **b)** $5,500 **c)** $7,040
11. 5.8, 4.6, <u>3.4</u>, 2.2, <u>1</u>, <u>−0.2</u>; SV: 5.8 Op: −1.2
13. $\frac{1}{3}$, 1, $1\frac{2}{3}$, $2\frac{1}{3}$, 3, $3\frac{2}{3}$; SV: $\frac{1}{3}$ Op: $+\frac{2}{3}$ **15.** $x = −42$ **17.** $x = 8$
19. $x = -\frac{3}{2}$

Lesson 11

1. +2 bugs per day **3.** $50\frac{2}{3}$ steps per minute **5.** ROC: +4; SV:5
7. ROC: +1; SV: −3 **9.** ROC: −2; SV: −1

11.

x	y
0	1
1	9
2	17
3	25
4	33
5	41

13.

x	y
−2	18
−1	13
0	8
1	3
3	−7
6	−22

15. a) 12 ants **b)** 30 ants **c)** 282 ants **17.** Answers may vary
19. Answers may vary

Lesson 12

1. $y = -6 + 8x$ **3.** $y = 7.1x$ **5.** $y = -10$ **7.** y-int = 4; ROC = +8; $y = 4 + 8x$ **9.** y-int = 6; ROC = +2; $y = 6 + 2x$ **11.** y-int = 7; ROC = +4; $y = 7 + 4x$ **13. a)** 2 problems per minute **b)** 12 **c)** $y = 12 + 2x$ **d)** minutes **e)** problems finished
15. a) 65 **b)** 0 **c)** $y = 65$
17. y-int = -1; ROC = +3; $y = -1 + 3x$

x	y
3	8
4	11

19. y-int = 14; ROC = +11; $y = 14 + 11x$

x	y
5	69
7	91

21.

x	$-2x + 7$	Output
-2	$-2(-2) + 7$	11
-1	$-2(-1) + 7$	9
0	$-2(0) + 7$	7
3	$-2(3) + 7$	1
5	$-2(5) + 7$	-3

23. 35 per hour
25. 12.5 points per assignment

Lesson 13

1. y-int = 8; ROC = +2 **3.** y-int = -4; ROC = +1 **5.** y-int = 0; ROC = $-\frac{1}{4}$ **7.** y-int = -8; ROC = $\frac{2}{3}$ **9.** y-int = 2; ROC = $-\frac{4}{7}$

11.

x	$x + 9$	y
-4	$-4 + 9$	5
0	$0 + 9$	9
2	$2 + 9$	11
5	$5 + 9$	14
21	$21 + 9$	30

13.

x	y
-3	9
-1	3
6	-18
10	-30
20	-60

15.

x	y
-4	5
-3	5
0	5
1	5
5	5

17. a)

x seconds	y meters run
10	68
25	170
40	272
60	408
100	680

b) ≈ 59 seconds; Answers may vary **c)** 3,600 seconds
d) 24,480 meters **e)** 15.3 miles **f)** Not reasonable. One could not sprint that far. **19.** $7\frac{1}{2}$ or 7.5 **21.** $x = -6$ **23.** $x = 3$
25. $x = -11$ **27.** $x = 3$

Lesson 14

1. $m = -3$ **3.** $m =$ undefined **5.** $m = 0$ **7.** negative **9.** zero **11.** positive **13. a)**

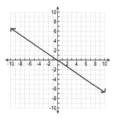

b)

c) They are the same. Yes. Same as both.

15. See student work **17.** Answers may vary

19. Answers may vary
21. 21 feet **23.** $\frac{2}{3}$
25. 9 **27.** Undefined

Lesson 15

1. $\frac{3}{2}$ **3.** 0 **5.** Undefined **7.** 0 **9.** -2 **11. a)** $\frac{4}{5}$ **b)** 0.8
c)

x	y
3	8
4	8.8
5	9.6
6	10.4
7	11.2
8	12

d) Six. Limitless

13. $-\frac{2}{5}$ or -0.4 **15. a)** $-\frac{1}{3}$ **b)** Amount of pop draining out of the bottle per hour **c)** 6 hours **17.** F **19.** B **21.** G

Block 2 Review

1. 8, 1, -6, <u>−13</u>, <u>−20</u>, <u>−27</u>; SV: 8; Op: − 7 **3.** 7, 7.6, <u>8.2</u>, <u>8.8</u>, 9.4, <u>10</u>; SV: 7; Op: +0.6 **5.** SV: 18; Op: −13; 9th term: −86

7. a) 6   **b)** 10, 14 **c)** SV: 6; Op: +4 **d)** 30

9. SV: 2; Op: $+\frac{1}{2}$

x	y
0	2
1	$2\frac{1}{2}$
2	3
3	$3\frac{1}{2}$
4	4
5	$4\frac{1}{2}$
6	5

11. a) Answers may vary

b) Answers may vary **13. a)** SV: 3.35; Op: +0.40 **b)**

x	y
0	3.35
1	3.75
2	4.15
3	4.55
4	4.95
5	5.35

c) **d)** ≈ 17 years **15.** 45 miles per hour

17. SV: 2; ROC: +7 **19.** SV: 13; ROC: +4 **21.** $y = −2 + 6x$
23. $y = 1 + 3.8x$ **25.** ROC: +3.5; y-int: 9.9; $y = 9.9 + 3.5x$
27. a) \$42 **b)** −\$3.10 **c)** $y = 42 − 3.1x$ **29.** ROC = −6;
y-int = 7 **31.** ROC = 2; y-int = 7 **33.** ROC = 0; y-int = 8

35.

x	y
0	4
3	5
4	$5\frac{1}{3}$
6	6
11	$7\frac{2}{3}$

37. See student work; $m = \frac{1}{3}$

39. See student work; $m = −2$
41. Answers may vary.

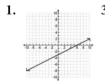

43. 9 feet **45.** $\frac{4}{3}$ **47.** 0 **49.** Undefined **51. a)** Rate of change; slope = −2 **b)** Slope formula; slope = $−\frac{5}{4}$
c) Slope triangle; slope = $\frac{3}{2}$

BLOCK 3

Lesson 16

1. **3.** **5.**

Lesson 16 (Continued)

7. **9.** **11. a)**

x	y
−2	−1
0	2
2	5
4	8

b) **c)** Answers may vary

13. Answers may vary
15.

x	y
1	5.5
2	8
3	10.5
4	13
5	15.5

b) + 2.5 **c)** (0, 3) **d)** $y = 2.5x + 3$
e) 28 inches
17. C **19.** B **21.** Undefined **23.** 1 **25.** $−\frac{5}{3}$

Lesson 17

1. $m = \frac{3}{4}$; $b = 3$; $y = \frac{3}{4}x + 3$ **3.** $m = 1$; $b = −3$; $y = x − 3$
5. $m = −\frac{2}{3}$; $b = 0$; $y = −\frac{2}{3}x$ **7. a)** $y = 6x + 20$ **b)** \$128
c) 32 months **9. a)** $y = 3x + 5$ **b)** 29 inches **c)** 14 weeks
11. a) $m \rightarrow y = \frac{1}{3}x + 2$; $n \rightarrow y = \frac{1}{3}x$; $p \rightarrow y = \frac{1}{3}x − 4$
b) Same slope **c)** Parallel **13.** False **15.** True **17.** True

Lesson 18

1. $y = \frac{6}{5}x + 8$ **3.** $y = x + 2$ **5. a)** $y = 50,000x + 3,400,000$
b) 4,400,000 people **7.** $y = −\frac{3}{4}x + 5$ **9.** $y = \frac{5}{2}x + 5$ **11.** $y = 8$
13. $y = 3x − 1$ **15.** $y = \frac{1}{3}x + 7$ **17.** $y = \frac{4}{5}x − 2$ **19.** $y = 3$
21. a) (2,9) and (8,12) **b)** $y = \frac{1}{2}x + 8$
c) 18 pounds; answers may vary **23. a)** (6,32) and (11,47)
b) $y = 3x + 14$ **c)** \$14 **d)** Cost per hour **e)** \$26
25. $y = −\frac{1}{3}x + 4$ **27.** **29.**

31. $y = 0.3x + 3$

Lesson 19

1. C **3.** E **5.** F **7.** $y = 4x + 21$ **9.** $y = \frac{1}{3}x + 1$ **11.** $y = −\frac{1}{2}x − 1$
13. $y = \frac{3}{4}x + 7$ **15.** $y = 4x + 9$ **17.** $y = \frac{1}{3}(x − 9) + 1$
19. $y = −3x + 10$ **21.** $y = −\frac{1}{2}x + 4$ **23.** $y = −5$ **25.** $y = −3x$

Lesson 20

1. $y = \frac{5}{2}x − 4$ **3.** $y = \frac{1}{2}x + 3$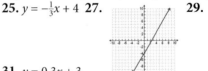

5. $y = \frac{4}{3}x − 2$ **7.** $x = 2$

Lesson 20 (Continued)

9. $y = 3x$ **11.** $y = x - 6$

13. Answers may vary **15.** Yes **17.** Yes **19.** No
21. No. She should have been charged $44. **23.** $-3x + y = 4$
25. $y = -2x + 6$ **27.** $y = 2$ **29.** $y = 2x$ **31.** $y = \frac{5}{2}x - 4$
33. $y = \frac{1}{3}x - 1$

Lesson 21

1.

x	y
-2	6
-1	3
0	2
1	3
2	6

3.

x	y
-2	-9
-1	-7
0	-5
1	-3
2	-1

5. Exponential

7. Non-linear; Exponential **9.** Non-linear; Inverse Variation
11. Linear **13.** 640 bacteria **15.** $x = 96$ **17.** $x = 6$ **19.** $x = 5$

21. **23.** **25.**

27. **29.**

Block 3 Review

1. **3.** **5.**

7. Answers may vary **9.** $m = -\frac{3}{5}$; $b = -1$; $y = -\frac{3}{5}x - 1$
11. a) $y = 2x + 7$ **b)** 21 inches **c)** 11 weeks
13. $y = -5x + 1$ **15.** $y = \frac{2}{5}x$ **17.** $y = \frac{1}{2}x - 2$ **19.** $y = \frac{5}{2}x + 5$
21. $y = \frac{1}{3}x + 2$ **23.** $y = -4$ **25. a)** (4,32) and (10,56)
b) $y = 4x + 16$ **c)** 16 **d)** Charge per hour **e)** $40
27. $y = -\frac{1}{2}x + 3$ **29.** $y = \frac{4}{5}x - 3$ **31.** $y = 3x + 5$
33. $y = 3x - 7$ **35.** $x = -2$

37. $y = 2x$ **39.** Yes **41.** Non-linear; Quadratic

43. Non-linear; Exponential **45.** Linear

BLOCK 4

Lesson 22

1. Same; infinite **3.** Parallel; none **5.** Same

7. Parallel; none **9.** Intersecting; one **11.** Same; infinite
13. Yes. The equations have different slopes **15.** Their paths
were the same. **17.** Answers may vary **19.** No. She gave
different slopes and similar y-intercepts. She needed to give
similar slopes and different y-intercepts. **21.** False **23.** True
25. $5x + 8$ **27.** $4x - 8$ **29.** $11x + 2y$

Lesson 23

1. a) Put both in slope-intercept form. **b)** graph **c)** Find the
point of intersection **d)** Substitute back in and check.
3. (-1,3) **5.** No **7.** Yes **9.** (4,5) **11.** (6,4) **13.** (3,3) **15.** (6,4)
17. No solution. Parallel lines. **19. a)** $y = 2x + 2y = 42$
b) $y = 2x + 3$ **c)** **d)** length = 15 *ft*; width = 6 *ft*

21. Intersecting; one **23.** Parallel; none
25. Intersecting; one

Lesson 24

1. (1, 2)

$y = 3x - 1$		$y = -2x + 4$	
x	y	x	y
0	-1	0	4
1	2	1	2
2	5	2	0
3	8	3	-2

3. They were getting further apart. **5.** (1,3) **7.** (-4,-2) **9.** (0,6)
11. a) $y = 15x + 100$

b) $y = -35x + 400$ **c)**

Carlos' Savings Account Balance		Ana's Savings Account Balance	
Months, x	Total Savings, y	Months, x	Total Savings, y
0	$100	0	$400
1	$115	1	$365
2	$130	2	$330
3	$145	3	$295
4	$160	4	$260
5	$175	5	$225
6	$190	6	$190
7	$205	7	$155
8	$220	8	$120

d) After 6 months. They will both have $190. **13.** 6 lawns
15. $x = \frac{3}{2}$ **17.** $x = -5$ **19.** $x = -2$

Lesson 25

1. x in #2 **3.** y in #2 **5.** Sometimes the intersection point is not an integer or it can be hard to see on the graph **7.** $(-1,2)$
9. $(6,-2)$ **11.** $(-7,8)$ **13.** $(-1,-6)$ **15.** $(-3,-1)$
17. a) $x + y = 46$; $x - y = 12$ **b)** 29 & 17
19. a) Tad: $6x + y = 67$; Timothy: $4x + 3y = 54$ **b)** $(10.5,4)$
c) $10.50 for a can of paint; $4.00 for a brush
21. Intersecting; one **23.** Intersecting; one
25. Parallel; none

Lesson 26

1. x; 0-step **3.** y; 1-step; multiply the first or second equation by -1. **5.** y; 2-step; multiply the first equation by 3 and the second equation by 2. **7.** She did not make it so the x or y coefficients were opposites. **9.** $(-2,3)$ **11.** $(5,-3)$ **13.** $\left(0, -\frac{1}{2}\right)$
15. $\left(\frac{3}{4}, 1\right)$ **17. a)** $3x + y = 29$; $x + 2y = 18$ **b)** One block is 8 and the other is 5 **19.** $(5,2)$ **21.** $(4,0)$ **23.** $(3,-1)$

Lesson 27

1. Elimination. The x's are already opposites and in standard form. **3.** Graphing. Both equations are in slope-intercept form. **5.** Elimination; $(4,-2)$ **7.** Elimination; $(3,3)$
9. Substitution; $(2,4)$ **11.** Elimination; $(-2,-6)$
13. Substitution; $(1,2.5)$

Lesson 28

1. x = weeks; y = total savings; Manny: $y = 85x + 200$;
Susan: $y = 100x + 95$ **3.** w = width of the garden;
l = length of the garden; $2w + 2l = 184$; $w = 2l$ **5.** x = number of snaps; y = total cost; Old machine: $y = 0.12x + 1{,}100$
New machine: $y = 0.09x + 1520$; $(14000,2780)$; The company would need to attach at least 14,000 snaps to make the new machine worthwhile. **7.** x = Family A's total;
y = Family B's total; $x + y = 1{,}640$; $x = 2y + 182$; $(1154, 486)$;
One family made $1,154 and one family made $486.
9. x = price of a gallon of ice cream; y = price of a container of strawberries; Jeremiah: $3x + 4y = 19.50$;
Gary: $5x + 2y = 22$; $(3.5, 2.25)$; A gallon of ice cream costs $3.50; A container of strawberries costs $2.25.
11. x = number of hours; y = total miles traveled;
Nancy: $y = 50x + 72$; Pedro: $y = 62x$; $(6, 372)$; He will catch up with her after 6 hours. **13.** Yes **15.** $(-6,-9)$ **17.** $(6,2)$
19. $(6,-3)$

Block 4 Review

1. Intersecting; one solution **3.** Parallel; no solutions
5. Parallel; no solutions **7.** Yes **9.** Yes **11.** $(-2, 0)$ **13.** $(6, -2)$

15. $(-4, -9)$

$y = -5 + x$		$y = 3x + 3$	
x	y	x	y
-5	-10	-5	-12
-4	-9	-4	-9
-3	-8	-3	-6
-2	-7	-2	-3

17. $(-2, 9)$

Block 4 Review (Continued)

19. a) $y = 400 - 20x$ **b)** $y = 100 + 40x$

c)

Evan's Balance		Lisa's Balance	
Months, x	Total Savings, y	Months, x	Total Savings, y
0	$400	0	$100
1	$380	1	$140
2	$360	2	$180
3	$340	3	$220
4	$320	4	$260
5	$300	5	$300
6	$280	6	$340

d) After 5 months they will both have $300. **21.** $(-3, 0)$
23. a) $x + y = 79$ represents the total number of Mr. James and Mr. Peters' cows; $x = 3y - 5$ represents 5 less than three times Mr. Peters' amount. **b)** $(58, 21)$; Mr. James = 58 cows; Mr. Peters = 21 cows **25.** y; 1-step; multiply the first equation by 2 **27.** $(-1, 6)$ **29.** $(1.5,4)$ **31.** Elimination; $(4, -2)$
33. Graphing; $(3, -4)$ **35.** Substitution; $(-6, 0)$
37. x = number of hours; y = total cost of rental;
A: $y = 2.5x + 8$; B: $y = x + 14$; $(4, 18)$; After 4 hours they are the same amount; Rentals are $18 for both companies after 4 hours. **39.** x = months passed; y = total amount in savings account; Jamal: $y = 24x + 46$; Emily: $y = -15x + 319$; $(7, 214)$;
After 7 months they will both have $214 in their accounts.

INDEX

PROBLEM - SOLVING

UNDERSTAND THE SITUATION

- ▶ Read then re-read the problem.
- ▶ Identify what the problem is asking you to find.
- ▶ Locate the key information.

PLAN YOUR APPROACH

Choose a strategy to solve the problem:

- ▶ Guess, check and revise
- ▶ Use an equation
- ▶ Use a formula
- ▶ Draw a picture
- ▶ Draw a graph
- ▶ Make a table
- ▶ Make a chart
- ▶ Make a list
- ▶ Look for patterns
- ▶ Compute or simplify

STOP AND THINK

- ▶ Did you answer the question that was asked?
- ▶ Does your answer make sense?
- ▶ Does your answer have the correct units?
- ▶ Look back over your work and correct any mistakes.

SOLVE THE PROBLEM

- ▶ Use your strategy to solve the problem.
- ▶ Show all work.

ANSWER THE QUESTION

- ▶ State your answer in a complete sentence.
- ▶ Include the appropriate units.

DEFEND YOUR ANSWER

Show that your answer is correct by doing one of the following:

- ▶ Use a second strategy to get the same answer.
- ▶ Verify that your first calculations are accurate by repeating your process.

MULTIPLE CHOICE
TEST TAKING STRATEGIES

#1: JUST DO IT

- I know how to do the problem.
- I can <u>solve the problem</u> to find the answer listed.

#2: WORK BACKWARDS

- I can <u>use the choices</u> given and work backwards.

#3: EDUCATED GUESS

- I am not sure how to do the problem.
- I can <u>eliminate at least one choice</u> that is not correct before I guess.

(A)   (C)
(B̶)   (D)

#4: PURE GUESS

- I have no idea how to do the problem.
- I have to <u>guess</u>.

SYMBOLS

Algebra and Number Operations

SYMBOL	MEANING
$+$	Plus or positive
$-$	Minus or negative
$5 \times n, 5 \cdot n, 5n, 5(n)$	Times (multiplication)
$3 \div 4, 4\overline{)3}, \frac{3}{4}$	Divided by (division)
$=$	Is equal to
$\approx$	Is approximately
$<$	Is less than
$>$	Is greater than
$\%$	Percent
$a : b$ or $\frac{a}{b}$	Ratio of a to b
$5.\overline{2}$	Repeating decimal (5.222…)
$\geq$	Is greater than or equal to
$\leq$	Is less than or equal to
x^n	The nth power of x
(a, b)	Ordered pair where a is the x-coordinate and b is the y-coordinate
$\pm$	Plus or minus
$\sqrt{x}$	Square root of x
$\neq$	Not equal to
$x \stackrel{?}{=} y$	Is x equal to y?
$\lvert x \rvert$	Absolute value of x
$P(A)$	Probability of event A

Geometry and Measurement

SYMBOL	MEANING
$\cong$	Is congruent to
$\sim$	Is similar to
$\angle$	Angle
$m\angle$	Measure of angle
$\triangle ABC$	Triangle ABC
$\overline{AB}$	Line segment AB
$\overrightarrow{AB}$	Ray AB
AB	Length of AB
π	Pi (approximately $\frac{22}{7}$ or 3.14)
$^\circ$	Degree

OREGON STATE ASSESSMENT FORMULAS

Reprinted from the Oregon Test Administration Manual with permission from the Oregon Department of Education.

MEASUREMENTS

1 meter = 100 centimeters	1 gram = 1000 milligrams	1 liter = 1000 cubic centimeters
1 kilometer = 1000 meters	1 kilogram = 1000 grams	
		1 cup = 8 fluid ounces
1 yard = 3 feet	1 pound = 16 ounces	1 pint = 2 cups
1 mile = 5280 feet	1 ton = 2000 pounds	1 quart = 2 pints
1 hour = 60 minutes		1 gallon = 4 quarts
1 minute = 60 seconds		

AREA (A)

$A = lw$

$A = bh$

$A = \frac{1}{2}bh$

$A = \pi r^2$
$C = 2\pi r$
Length of an arc $= \frac{m}{360} \times 2\pi r$

$A = \frac{1}{2}h(b_1 + b_2)$

SURFACE AREA (SA) and VOLUME (V)

$V = lwh$
$SA = 2(lw + wh + lh)$

$V = \pi r^2 h$
$SA = 2\pi rh + 2\pi r^2$

$V = \frac{4}{3}\pi r^3$
$SA = 4\pi r^2$

$V = \frac{1}{3}(BA)(h)$
$SA = (LA) + (BA)$

LA = Lateral Area
BA = Base Area

$V = \frac{1}{3}(BA)(h) = \frac{1}{3}(\pi r^2)(h)$

$SA = LA + BA = (\pi rl) + (\pi r^2)$

$a^2 + b^2 = c^2$

$d = \sqrt{(x_2 - x_1)^2 + (y_2 - y_1)^2}$